New Elementary MATHEMATICS

SYLLABUS D

WORKBOOK

Low Wai Cheng
B. Sc., Dip. Ed.

PAN PACIFIC PUBLICATIONS (S) PTE LTD

PAN PACIFIC PUBLICATIONS (S) PTE LTD
16 Fan Yoong Road Singapore 629793

First published 2000

ISBN 981-208-532-7

Printed by Seng Lee Press Pte Ltd, Singapore

PREFACE

New Elementary Mathematics Workbook 4, a supplement to the textbooks *New Elementary Mathematics 4A* and *4B*, is specially written to provide students with additional practice.

Each *Revision Exercise* covers a chapter in the textbook and attempts have been made to integrate the appropriate concepts of different topics into a single question. *Test Papers* are provided after every two revision exercises to help reinforce concepts learnt. *Assessment Papers* have also been included to prepare students for the final examination.

CONTENTS

CHAPTER 1 Loci

1. For each of the following cases, sketch and describe the locus of the goat if it walks about, keeping the rope taut. Find also the area of the region that the goat can reach.
   (a) The goat is tethered to a tree by a rope 2 m long.
   (b) The goat is tethered by a rope $1\frac{1}{2}$ m long to a ring which slides on a rail 4 m long.
   (c) The goat is tethered to a bolt in the middle of a wall 8 m long by a rope 3 m long.
   (d) The goat is tethered to a bolt in the middle of a wall of a square pillar of side 1 m by a rope
   (i) 1 m long,
   (ii) 2 m long.
   (e) The goat is tethered to a bolt on one corner of a square pillar of side 1 m by a rope
   (i) 2 m long,
   (ii) $3\frac{1}{2}$ m long,
   and moves in an anticlockwise direction.

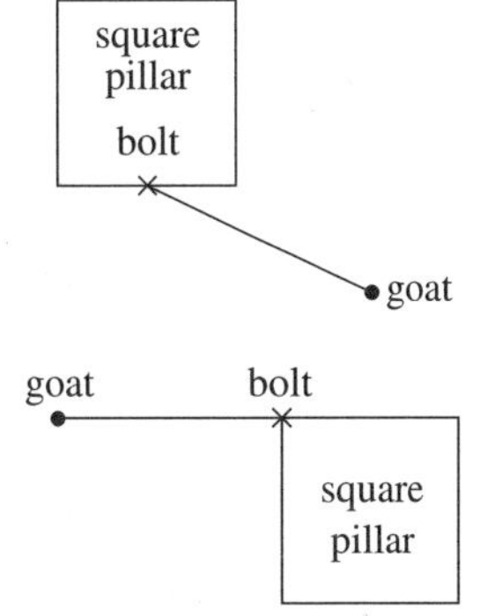

2. Given a square $ABCD$, sketch and describe the locus of a variable point P moving within the square such that
   (a) P is equidistant from AB and AD,
   (b) P is nearer to BC than to CD.

3. Given a triangle ABC, sketch and describe the locus of a point P moving within the triangle such that
   (a) P is 3 cm from B,
   (b) $BP \leqslant 3$ cm.

4. Given a semicircle with diameter AB, sketch and describe the locus of a point P moving within the semicircle such that
   (a) $AP = BP$,
   (b) $AP \leqslant BP$.

5. Draw a square $ABCD$ of side 6 cm.
   (a) Within the square,
   (i) construct and describe the locus of a point P such that $A\hat{P}B = 90°$,
   (ii) construct and describe the locus of a point Q such that area of $\triangle AQB = 6$ cm^2.
   (b) X is a point which moves inside the square so that $A\hat{X}B > 90°$ and area of $\triangle AXB \geqslant 6$ cm^2. Indicate clearly by shading the region in which X must lie.

6. **(a)** Construct, in a single diagram,

(i) a triangle ABC with sides $AB = 7$ cm, $AC = 8$ cm and $BC = 9$ cm,

(ii) the locus of points which are 2.3 cm from BC,

(iii) the locus of points which are equidistant from B and C.

(b) The locus of a point P is such that P lies inside $\triangle ABC$ and P is more than 2.3 cm from BC. Shade the region of P that represents $PB < PC$.

7.

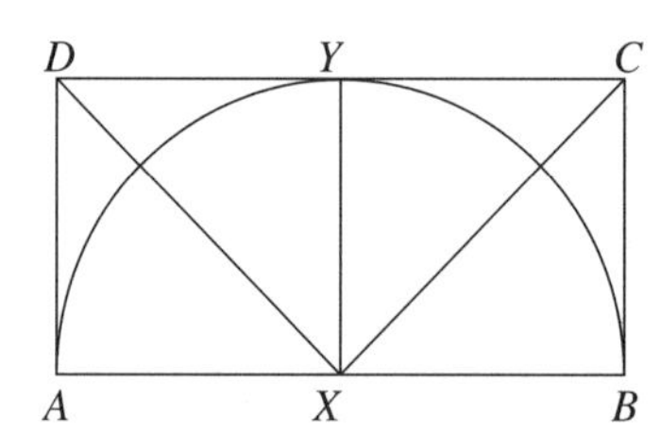

A semicircle, centre X, touches the side CD of the rectangle $ABCD$ at Y. The point P lies inside the rectangle such that

$$A\hat{P}B \leqslant 90°,\ PB \leqslant PY \text{ and } PB \leqslant PA.$$

Indicate clearly, by shading, the region in which the point P must lie.

8. **(a)** Using the rhombus provided, construct the locus of points within the rhombus that are equidistant

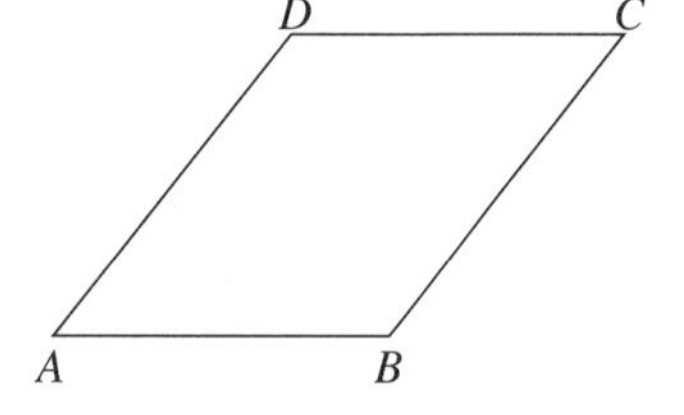

(i) from AB and AD,

(ii) from A and B,

(iii) from A as the points B and D.

(b) The position of a point X, which lies inside the rhombus, is such that $AX \leqslant AB$, $AX \geqslant XB$ and X is nearer to AB than to AD. Shade the region representing the set of possible positions of X.

9. Construct the triangle ABC such that $AB = 10$ cm, $AC = 6$ cm and $B\hat{A}C = 90°$.

(a) Calculate the area of $\triangle ABC$.

(b) On the same diagram, and on the same side of AB as C, draw the locus of points

(i) P such that area of $\triangle ABP = \frac{3}{2}$ area of $\triangle ABC$,

(ii) Q such that area of $\triangle AQC = \frac{1}{2}$ area of $\triangle ABC$,

(iii) R such that area of $\triangle ARB = 5\ \text{cm}^2$.

(c) X is the point of intersection of the locus of P and the locus of Q. Find the area of $ABXC$.

10. **(a)** Construct a triangle XYZ such that $XY = 9$ cm, $XZ = 7$ cm and $YZ = 10.5$ cm.

(b) On the same diagram, and on the same side of XY as Z, draw the locus of points which are 4 cm from XY.

(c) On the same diagram, draw the locus of points which are 4 cm from Z.

(d) P is the point inside the triangle such that $PZ = 4$ cm and the perpendicular distance from P to XY is 4 cm. Mark and label the point P. Measure and write down the length of PX.

(e) Q is the point inside the triangle which is less than 4 cm from XY but more than 4 cm from Z. Shade the region on the diagram in which Q must lie.

11. Construct the triangle ABC in which $AB = 9.5$ cm, $A\hat{C}B = 100°$ and $A\hat{B}C = 28°$.

(a) Measure and write down the length of BC.

(b) On your diagram, draw and label the locus of points which are

(i) 3 cm from C,

(ii) equidistant from A and B,

(iii) equidistant from AC to AB.

(c) P is the locus of points which lies inside $\triangle ABC$, and is such that $PC \geqslant 3$ cm, $PB \leqslant PA$ and P is nearer to AB than to AC. Shade the region in which P must lie.

12. **(a)** Construct the triangle XYZ such that $XY = 7.7$ cm, $Y\hat{X}Z = 60°$ and $X\hat{Z}Y = 90°$.

(b) On the same diagram, construct the locus of points

(i) 3 cm from Y,

(ii) Q such that $X\hat{Q}Y = 90°$.

(c) Mark on your diagram, a point P, which is 3 cm from Y and such that $X\hat{P}Y = 90°$.

(d) A point R is such that RY is less than 3 cm and $X\hat{R}Y$ is less than 90°. Shade the region in which R must lie.

13. **(a)** Using ruler and compasses only, construct triangle XYZ where the base $XY = 9$ cm, $YZ = 7$ cm and $XZ = 10.5$ cm. Measure, and write down, the size of $X\hat{Y}Z$.

(b) On your diagram, draw the locus of points that are

(i) equidistant from XY and XZ,

(ii) equidistant from XY and YZ.

(c) Hence, draw the circle that is inscribed in the triangle. Write down the radius of the circle.

(d) The point P, inside the triangle, is nearer to XY than to XZ and YZ. Also, the radius of the circle is less than the length of OP, where O is the centre of the circle. Shade the region of your diagram in which P must lie.

14. **(a)** Construct the triangle DEF in which $DE = 8$ cm, $EF = 6$ cm and $DF = 9$ cm. Measure, and write down, the size of $D\hat{F}E$.

(b) On your diagram,

(i) draw the locus of points that are equidistant from D and E,

(ii) by making a further construction, mark clearly with the letter O, the centre of the circle that passes through the three vertices of the triangle,

(iii) draw this circle,

(iv) measure and write down the radius of the circle.

(c) The position of a point P, which lies inside the triangle, is such that $DP < FP$, $DP < EP$ and $OP < OD$. Indicate clearly, by shading, the region in which the point P must lie.

15. Construct, and label, the triangle STU in which $ST = 8$ cm, $S\hat{T}U = 54°$ and $TU = 6.5$ cm.

(a) Measure, and write down,

(i) the length of SU,

(ii) the size of $S\hat{U}T$.

(b) On your diagram,

(i) construct the position of the point O which is equidistant from S, T and U,

(ii) measure and write down the length of OS.

(c) Draw the locus of points on the same side of SU as T, such that SU subtends an angle of 54°.

(d) Mark and clearly label the point X such that $SX = TX$ and $S\hat{X}U = 54°$.

16. **(a)** Construct an equilateral triangle LMN of side 5 cm.

(b) On your diagram, and on the same side of LM as N, construct

(i) the locus of points P such that $L\hat{P}M = 30°$,

(ii) the locus of points Q such that area of $\triangle LQM$ = area of $\triangle LMN$.

(c) On your diagram, label the points X and Y such that $L\hat{X}M = L\hat{Y}M = 30°$ and area of $\triangle LXM$ = area of $\triangle LYM$ = area of $\triangle LMN$.

17. Construct the triangle GHI in which $G\hat{H}I = 90°$, $GH = 6$ cm and $GI = 10$ cm.

(a) Measure, and write down,

(i) the length of HI,

(ii) the size of $H\hat{G}I$.

(b) On your diagram, and on the same side of GI as H, construct

(i) the locus of points X, such that $G\hat{X}I = 90°$,

(ii) the locus of points Y, such that area of $\triangle GYI$ = area of $\triangle GHI$.

(c) On your diagram, label

(i) the point P such that area of $\triangle GPI$ = area of $\triangle GHI$ and $P\hat{G}I = 90°$,

(ii) the point Q such that area of $\triangle GQI$ = area of $\triangle GHI$ and $QI = GI$.

18. **(a)** Construct the triangle DEF in which DE = 5 cm, EF = 6.5 cm and $D\hat{E}F = 110°$.

(b) On your diagram, construct the locus of points

(i) on the same side of DF as E, at which DF subtends an angle of 110°,

(ii) which are equidistant from DE and DF.

(c) Mark on your diagram the point X which is equidistant from DE and DF and such that $D\hat{X}F = 110°$.

(d) Q is a point, outside the triangle, which is nearer to DF than to DE and $D\hat{Q}F$ is more than 110°. Shade the region on the diagram in which Q must lie.

19. **(a)** Construct the triangle LMN such that LM = 8 cm and $L\hat{M}N = N\hat{L}M = 50°$.

(b) On the same diagram and on the same side of LM as N, construct

(i) the locus of points which are 4 cm from LM,

(ii) the locus of points such that LM subtends an angle of 40°.

(c) Mark a point P on the diagram such that the area of $\triangle LMP$ = 16 cm^2 and $L\hat{P}M = 40°$.

20. Construct the triangle LMN in which LM = 7 cm, $L\hat{M}N = 45°$ and $M\hat{L}N = 75°$.

(a) Write down the size of $L\hat{N}M$.

(b) On the same diagram, construct the locus of points which are

(i) equidistant from L and M,

(ii) equidistant from L and N.

(c) Mark clearly, on your diagram, the point X which is equidistant from L, M and N.

(i) Measure and write down the length of LX.

(ii) Draw a circle passing through L, M and N.

(d) On the same diagram, draw the locus of the point P on the same side of LM as N and such that the area of $\triangle LMP$ is $10\frac{1}{2}$ cm^2.

(e) Mark, and label clearly,

(i) a point Q such that $L\hat{Q}M = 60°$ and area of $\triangle LQM = 10\frac{1}{2}$ cm^2,

(ii) a point R such that $LR = NR$ and area of $\triangle LRM = 10\frac{1}{2}$ cm^2.

21. **(a)** Construct an isosceles triangle UVW in which $UV = UW$ = 6 cm and $U\hat{V}W = 35°$.

(b) On your diagram, construct the locus of points which are

(i) 4 cm from V,

(ii) equidistant from UW and VW.

(c) On your diagram,

(i) label the point P, inside $\triangle UVW$, which is 4 cm from V and equidistant from UW and VW,

(ii) measure and write down the length of UP.

(d) The point Q, inside $\triangle UVW$, is greater than 4 cm from V and nearer to VW than to UW. Indicate clearly, by shading, the region of your diagram in which Q must lie.

22. Construct, and label, the triangle ABC in which $AB = 9$ cm, $A\hat{B}C = 35°$ and $B\hat{A}C = 90°$.

(a) On your diagram,

(i) draw and label the locus of points which are equidistant from B and C,

(ii) on the same side of AB as C, construct the locus of point P such that $A\hat{P}B = 55°$.

(b) Q is a point which is equidistant from B and C and is such that $A\hat{Q}B = 55°$.

(i) Label the point Q on your diagram.

(ii) Measure, and write down, the length of BQ.

(c) R is a point outside the triangle ABC and is such that $BR \leqslant CR$ and $A\hat{R}B \geqslant 55°$. Shade the region on your diagram in which R must lie.

23. AB is a line segment 8 cm long.

(a) Sketch and decide the locus of points which are

(i) 5 cm from A,

(ii) equidistant from A and B,

(iii) 6 cm from AB.

(b) **(i)** On your sketch, label the points P and Q, each of which is 5 cm from A and equidistant from A and B.

(ii) Find the length of PQ.

(c) The point R is equidistant from A and B and 6 cm from AB. Find the length of AR.

24. Describe completely the locus of points in two dimensions which are

(a) 5 cm from a given straight line l,

(b) 6 cm from a given point O,

(c) equidistant from two given points A and B.

CHAPTER 2 Vectors

1. Express the vectors **a**, **b** and **c** in terms of **r**.

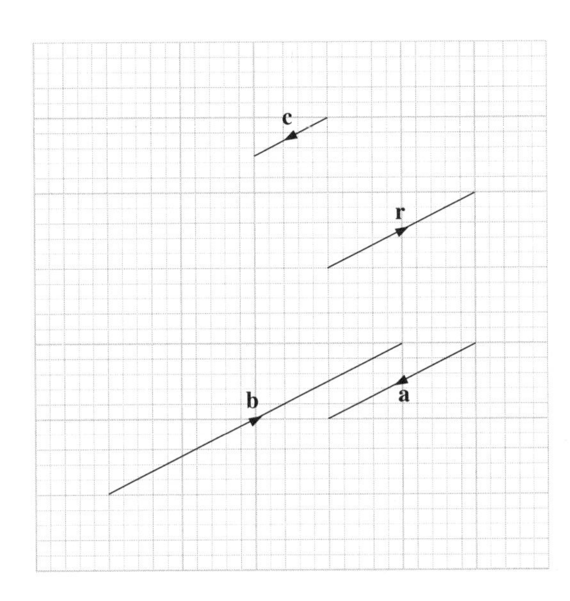

2.

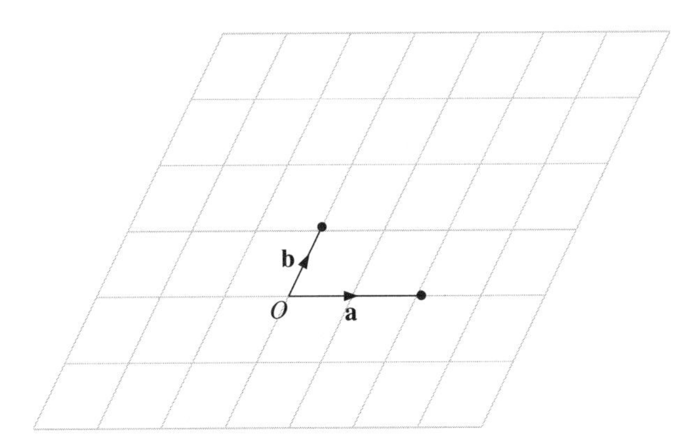

Copy the diagram and on it draw from O, the vector equal to

(a) $\frac{1}{2}\mathbf{a} + 3\mathbf{b}$, **(b)** $2\mathbf{a} - \mathbf{b}$, **(c)** $4\mathbf{b} - \mathbf{a}$.

3. $ABCD$ is a quadrilateral. Find the single vector which is equivalent to

(a) $\overrightarrow{AB} + \overrightarrow{BC}$, **(b)** $\overrightarrow{AB} + \overrightarrow{BC} + \overrightarrow{CD}$,

(c) $\overrightarrow{AB} + \overrightarrow{DA}$, **(d)** $\overrightarrow{BD} - \overrightarrow{CD}$.

4.

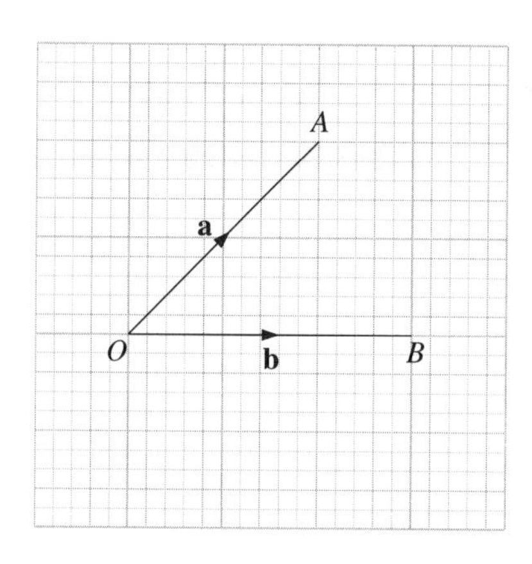

(a) Copy the figure and on it construct

(i) $\overrightarrow{OP} = 3\mathbf{a} + 2\mathbf{b}$,

(ii) $\overrightarrow{OQ} = 2\mathbf{b} - 2\mathbf{a}$.

(b) If $\overrightarrow{OR} = \mathbf{a} + \frac{2}{3}\mathbf{b}$, what can you tell about the points O, P and R?

(c) If $\overrightarrow{AS} = \frac{3}{2}\mathbf{a} + \mathbf{b}$, what can you tell about the lines AS and OP?

(d) If $\overrightarrow{BC} = \frac{1}{2}\mathbf{b} - \frac{1}{2}\mathbf{a}$, what can you tell about

(i) the points A, B and C,

(ii) the lines BC and OQ?

5. In $\triangle ABC$, $\overrightarrow{AB} = \mathbf{a}$ and $\overrightarrow{BC} = \mathbf{b}$. D is the midpoint of AB. Express the vectors $\overrightarrow{CA}$ and $\overrightarrow{DC}$ in terms of $\mathbf{a}$ and $\mathbf{b}$.

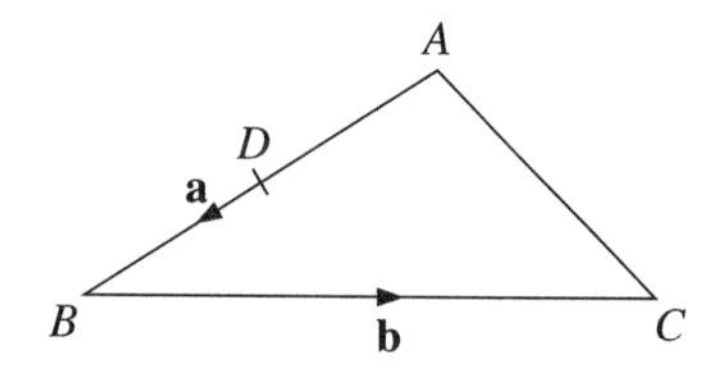

6. In the figure, $\overrightarrow{OA} = 2\mathbf{a}$, $\overrightarrow{OB} = \mathbf{b}$ and $\overrightarrow{OC} = -4\mathbf{a} + 3\mathbf{b}$.

(a) Express the vectors $\overrightarrow{AB}$ and $\overrightarrow{BC}$ in terms of $\mathbf{a}$ and $\mathbf{b}$.

(b) Hence show that the points A, B and C lie on a straight line.

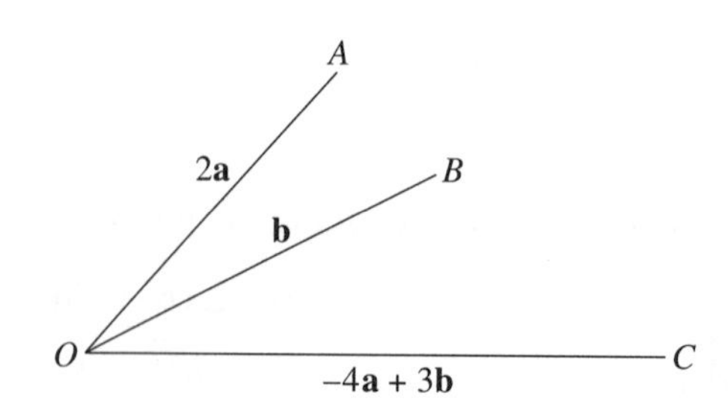

7. $ABCDEF$ is a regular hexagon with centre O. If $\overrightarrow{BC} = \mathbf{b}$ and $\overrightarrow{FC} = 2\mathbf{a}$, express the following in terms of $\mathbf{a}$ and $\mathbf{b}$.

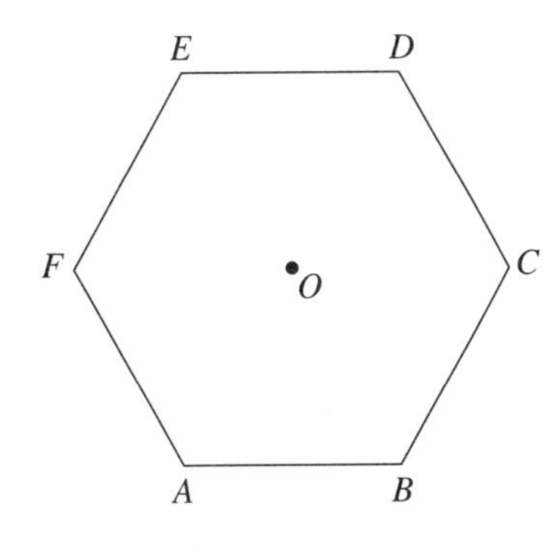

(a) $\overrightarrow{OF}$

(b) $\overrightarrow{FD}$

(c) $\overrightarrow{DE}$

(d) $\overrightarrow{AB}$

(e) $\overrightarrow{CD}$

(f) $\overrightarrow{BE}$

8. OAB is a triangle and P is a point on AB such that $PB = 3PA$. Show that $4\overrightarrow{OP} = 3\overrightarrow{OA} + \overrightarrow{OB}$.

9. Two points A and B have position vectors $\mathbf{a}$ and $\mathbf{b}$ respectively relative to an origin O. The points P on OA and Q on AB are such that $OP = 3PA$ and $2AQ = 3QB$. Express $\overrightarrow{AP}$, $\overrightarrow{AQ}$ and $\overrightarrow{PQ}$ in terms of $\mathbf{a}$ and $\mathbf{b}$.

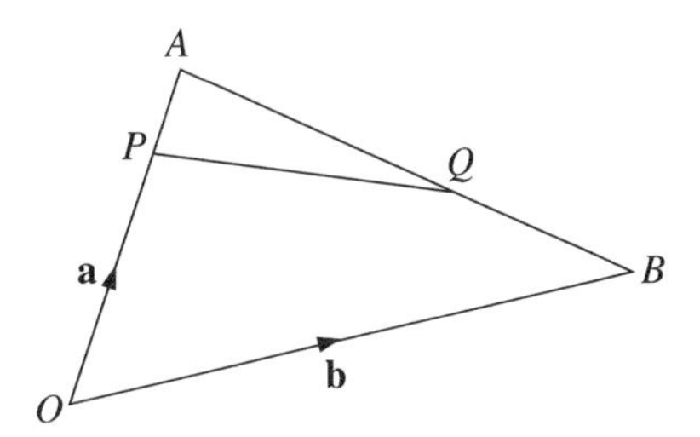

10. Given $\mathbf{a} = \begin{pmatrix} 2 \\ 1 \end{pmatrix}$ and $\mathbf{b} = \begin{pmatrix} 1 \\ -2 \end{pmatrix}$, express the following as column vectors.

(a) $\mathbf{a} + 5\mathbf{b}$

(b) $2\mathbf{a} - 3\mathbf{b}$

(c) $-\frac{3}{4}\mathbf{a} + \frac{1}{2}\mathbf{b}$

11. For each of the following vectors, find its magnitude.

(a) $\begin{pmatrix} -3 \\ 3 \end{pmatrix}$

(b) $\begin{pmatrix} 5 \\ 12 \end{pmatrix}$

(c) $\begin{pmatrix} 9 \\ -12 \end{pmatrix}$

12. A is the point $(1, -3)$ and B is the point $(2, 5)$.

(a) Find $|\overrightarrow{AB}|$.

(b) M is the midpoint of AB. Find the position vector of M relative to the origin O.

13. Find the value of h and of k if $\mathbf{a} = h\mathbf{b} + k\mathbf{c}$, where $\mathbf{a} = \begin{pmatrix} 7 \\ -16 \end{pmatrix}$, $\mathbf{b} = \begin{pmatrix} 3 \\ -2 \end{pmatrix}$ and $\mathbf{c} = \begin{pmatrix} 1 \\ 5 \end{pmatrix}$.

14. The position vectors of the points P, Q, R and S are $\begin{pmatrix} 4 \\ 3 \end{pmatrix}$, $\begin{pmatrix} 5 \\ 2 \end{pmatrix}$, $\begin{pmatrix} 2 \\ -2 \end{pmatrix}$ and $\begin{pmatrix} 4 \\ -4 \end{pmatrix}$ respectively.

(a) Express $\overrightarrow{PQ}$ and $\overrightarrow{RS}$ as column vectors.

(b) What can you tell about the lines PQ and RS?

15. The position vectors of the points A, B and C are $\mathbf{a} = \begin{pmatrix} 3 \\ -7 \end{pmatrix}$, $\mathbf{b} = \begin{pmatrix} 6 \\ 5 \end{pmatrix}$ and $\mathbf{c} = \begin{pmatrix} 7 \\ k \end{pmatrix}$. Find

(a) $\overrightarrow{AB}$,

(b) $\overrightarrow{BC}$,

(c) k if A, B and C are collinear.

16. O is the origin, P is the point (8, 5) and Q is the point (11, 13). $\overrightarrow{OP} = \mathbf{p}$ and $\overrightarrow{OQ} = \mathbf{q}$.

(a) Find the value of $|\overrightarrow{PQ}|$.

(b) Calculate the coordinates of the midpoint of PQ.

(c) R is the point such that $\overrightarrow{PR} = \frac{2}{3}\overrightarrow{PQ}$. Express $\overrightarrow{OR}$ in terms of $\mathbf{p}$ and $\mathbf{q}$.

17. The column vectors $\mathbf{a}$, $\mathbf{b}$ and $\mathbf{c}$ are defined by $\mathbf{a} = \begin{pmatrix} -6 \\ 8 \end{pmatrix}$, $\mathbf{b} = \begin{pmatrix} 3 \\ 7 \end{pmatrix}$ and $\mathbf{c} = \begin{pmatrix} p \\ q \end{pmatrix}$ respectively.

(a) Find $|\mathbf{a}|$.

(b) Express $\frac{3}{2}\mathbf{a} + 2\mathbf{b}$ as a column vector.

(c) Given that $\mathbf{a} - 2\mathbf{c} = 3\mathbf{b} + \mathbf{c}$, find the value of p and of q.

18. $\overrightarrow{AB} = \begin{pmatrix} 6 \\ -4 \end{pmatrix}$ and $\overrightarrow{CD} = \begin{pmatrix} 9 \\ k \end{pmatrix}$.

(a) Calculate $|\overrightarrow{AB}|$.

(b) Given that A is the point (3, 5), find the coordinates of the point B.

(c) Given that $\overrightarrow{CD}$ is parallel to $\overrightarrow{AB}$, find the value of k.

19. It is given that $\mathbf{u} = \begin{pmatrix} 5 \\ 6 \end{pmatrix}$ and $\mathbf{v} = \begin{pmatrix} 4 \\ -2 \end{pmatrix}$.

(a) Find the value of $|\mathbf{u} + \mathbf{v}|$.
(b) If $\mathbf{u} = 5\mathbf{v} - 2\mathbf{w}$, express $\mathbf{w}$ as a column vector.

20. $\overrightarrow{PQ} = \begin{pmatrix} 10 \\ -6 \end{pmatrix}$ and $\overrightarrow{PR} = \begin{pmatrix} -6 \\ 9 \end{pmatrix}$. Find

(a) $\overrightarrow{QR}$,
(b) $\overrightarrow{PX}$, given that $3\overrightarrow{PX} = 2\overrightarrow{RP}$.

21. $\mathbf{a} = \begin{pmatrix} -12 \\ 8 \end{pmatrix}$, $\mathbf{b} = \begin{pmatrix} 8 \\ -5 \end{pmatrix}$ and $\mathbf{c} = \begin{pmatrix} p \\ q \end{pmatrix}$.

(a) Express $2\mathbf{a} + 3\mathbf{b}$ as a column vector.
(b) Find $|\mathbf{a}|^2$.
(c) Given that $\mathbf{c}$ is parallel to $\mathbf{a}$, express p in terms of q.

22. $\overrightarrow{PQ} = \begin{pmatrix} 20 \\ -15 \end{pmatrix}$ and $\overrightarrow{RS} = \frac{2}{5}\overrightarrow{QP}$.

(a) Calculate $|\overrightarrow{PQ}|$.
(b) Express $\overrightarrow{RS}$ as a column vector.
(c) Given that P is the point (9, 11), find the coordinates of the point Q.
(d) Given that S is the point (–1, 0), find the coordinates of the point R.

23. It is given that $\overrightarrow{AB} = \begin{pmatrix} 16 \\ -9 \end{pmatrix}$ and $\overrightarrow{CD} = \begin{pmatrix} s \\ t \end{pmatrix}$.

(a) If $ABCD$ is a parallelogram, find the value of s and of t.
(b) P is a point on AB such that $AB = \frac{1}{3}BP$. Express $\overrightarrow{AP}$ as a column vector.
(c) If A is the point (10, –8), find the coordinates of P.

24. It is given that $\overrightarrow{OP} = \begin{pmatrix} -3 \\ 5 \end{pmatrix}$, $\overrightarrow{OQ} = \begin{pmatrix} 3 \\ u \end{pmatrix}$, $\overrightarrow{OR} = \begin{pmatrix} 5 \\ w \end{pmatrix}$, $\overrightarrow{OS} = \begin{pmatrix} x \\ 9 \end{pmatrix}$, $\overrightarrow{PQ} = \begin{pmatrix} u \\ v \end{pmatrix}$ and $3\overrightarrow{OP} = \overrightarrow{OR} + 2\overrightarrow{OS}$. Find the values of u, v, w and x.

25. It is given that A is the point (–2, 2), B is the point (5, 4) and $\overrightarrow{BC} = \begin{pmatrix} -2 \\ -5 \end{pmatrix}$.

(a) Express as column vectors
   (i) $\overrightarrow{AB}$,
   (ii) the position vector of C relative to the origin O.
(b) If $ABCD$ is a parallelogram, find the coordinates of the vertex D.

26. Given that $\overrightarrow{OA} = \begin{pmatrix} -4 \\ 3 \end{pmatrix}$, $\overrightarrow{AB} = \begin{pmatrix} 9 \\ 21 \end{pmatrix}$, M is the midpoint of $\overrightarrow{OA}$ and N is the point on AB such that $\overrightarrow{AN} = \frac{1}{2}\overrightarrow{NB}$,

(a) find the value of $|\overrightarrow{OB}|$, giving your answer correct to 1 decimal place,

(b) express as column vectors

(i) $\overrightarrow{AN}$,

(ii) $\overrightarrow{MN}$.

27. $OABC$ is a rhombus where O is the origin, $\overrightarrow{OA} = \begin{pmatrix} 0 \\ 13 \end{pmatrix}$ and $\overrightarrow{OC} = \begin{pmatrix} 5 \\ t \end{pmatrix}$. Find

(a) $|\overrightarrow{OA}|$,

(b) the value of t,

(c) the coordinates of the two possible positions of B.

28. In the diagram, $\overrightarrow{WZ} = \begin{pmatrix} 6 \\ 8 \end{pmatrix}$, $\overrightarrow{WX} = \begin{pmatrix} 0 \\ 3 \end{pmatrix}$ and Y is a point on XZ such that $XY = \frac{1}{3}XZ$. Express each of the following as a column vector.

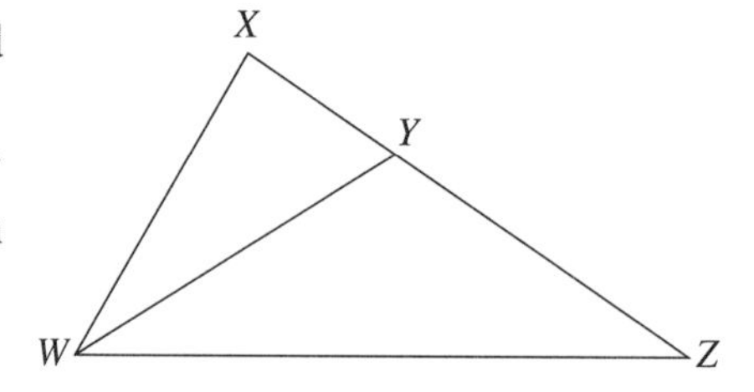

(a) $\overrightarrow{YZ}$

(b) $\overrightarrow{WY}$

29. In the diagram, P is the point (1, 2) and O is the origin.

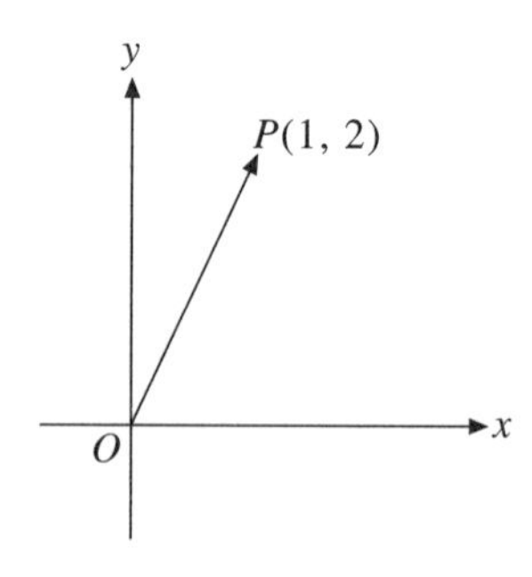

(a) The point P_1 is the reflection of P in the y-axis. Express $\overrightarrow{OP_1}$ as a column vector.

(b) The point P_2 lies on PO produced such that $\overrightarrow{OP_2} = h\overrightarrow{OP}$, where $h < 0$. Express $\overrightarrow{OP_2}$ as a column vector in terms of h.

(c) OP is rotated through an angle of 90° in a clockwise direction about O so that P is mapped onto P_3. Express $\overrightarrow{OP_3}$ as a column vector.

(d) Given that P_1P is parallel to P_2P_3, where $\overrightarrow{P_1P} = k\overrightarrow{P_2P_3}$, find the numerical value of h and of k.

30. In the diagram, P, Q, R and S are the midpoints of AB, AC, BC and BR respectively. Given that $\overrightarrow{AB} = \mathbf{b}$ and $\overrightarrow{AC} = \mathbf{c}$, express as simply as possible in terms of $\mathbf{b}$ and/or $\mathbf{c}$,

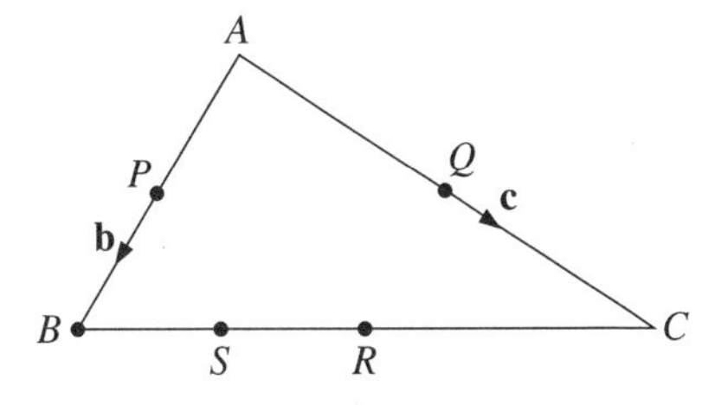

(a) $\overrightarrow{BC}$, **(b)** $\overrightarrow{BS}$,

(c) $\overrightarrow{CP}$, **(d)** $\overrightarrow{PQ}$,

(e) $\overrightarrow{AR}$, **(f)** $\overrightarrow{QS}$,

(g) $\overrightarrow{PR}$.

31. In the diagram, $\overrightarrow{OA} = 5\mathbf{a}$, $\overrightarrow{OB} = 10\mathbf{b}$ and X is a point on AB such that $\frac{AX}{XB} = \frac{2}{3}$.

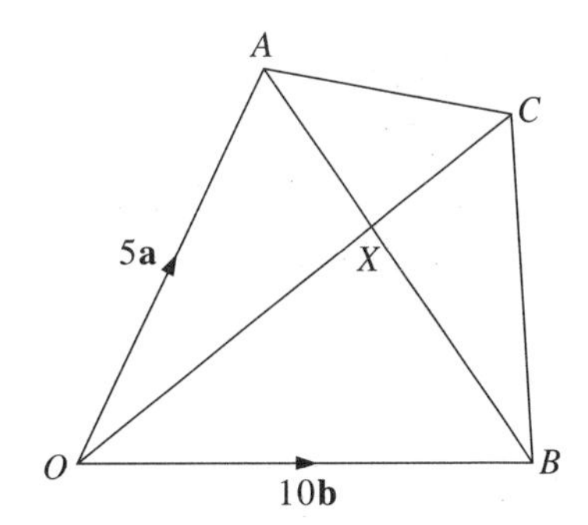

(a) Express in terms of $\mathbf{a}$ and $\mathbf{b}$, as simply as possible,

(i) $\overrightarrow{AB}$,

(ii) $\overrightarrow{AX}$,

(iii) $\overrightarrow{OX}$.

(b) Given that $\overrightarrow{AC} = h\overrightarrow{OB}$ and $\overrightarrow{OX} = k\overrightarrow{OC}$, form an equation connecting $\mathbf{a}$, $\mathbf{b}$, h and k and hence find the value of h and of k.

32. It is given that $\overrightarrow{OA} = 2\mathbf{a}$, $\overrightarrow{OP} = 3\mathbf{a} + 2\mathbf{b}$ and $\overrightarrow{AQ} = \mathbf{a} + \mathbf{b}$.

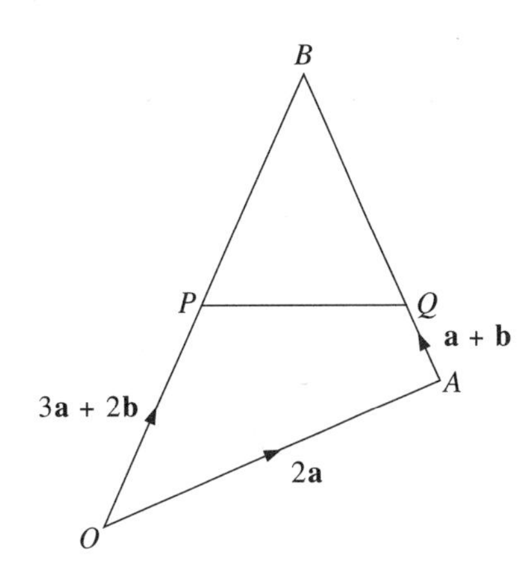

(a) Express as simply as possible, in terms of $\mathbf{a}$ and $\mathbf{b}$,

(i) $\overrightarrow{AP}$,

(ii) $\overrightarrow{PQ}$.

(b) Given that $\overrightarrow{OB} = h\overrightarrow{OP}$ and $\overrightarrow{AB} = k\overrightarrow{AQ}$, form an equation connecting $\mathbf{a}$, $\mathbf{b}$, h and k and hence find the value of h and of k.

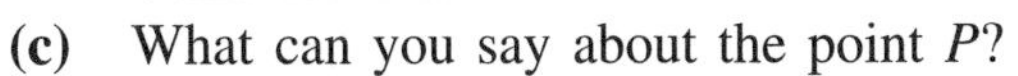

(c) What can you say about the point P?

(d) Find the numerical value of the ratio $\frac{AQ}{QB}$.

33. In the diagram, R divides OP in the ratio 1 : 2, S divides PQ in the ratio 1 : 3 and QR and OS meet at T.

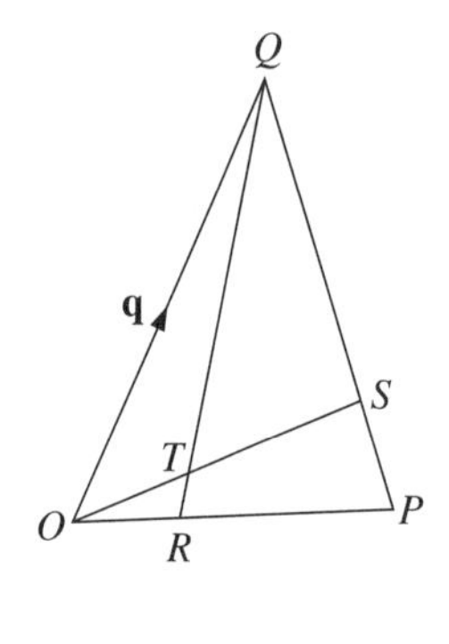

(a) If $\overrightarrow{OP} = \mathbf{p}$ and $\overrightarrow{OQ} = \mathbf{q}$, find the vectors $\overrightarrow{QR}$ and $\overrightarrow{OS}$ in terms of $\mathbf{p}$ and $\mathbf{q}$.

(b) Complete the following:

$\overrightarrow{OQ}$ + ________________ = $\overrightarrow{OT}$

(c) If $\overrightarrow{QT} = m\overrightarrow{QR}$ and $\overrightarrow{OT} = n\overrightarrow{OS}$, form an equation connecting m, n, $\mathbf{p}$ and $\mathbf{q}$. Hence solve the equation to find the value of m and of n.

(d) Express the vectors $\overrightarrow{QT}$ and $\overrightarrow{OT}$ in terms of $\mathbf{p}$ and $\mathbf{q}$ only.

34. In the diagram, ADC is a straight line.

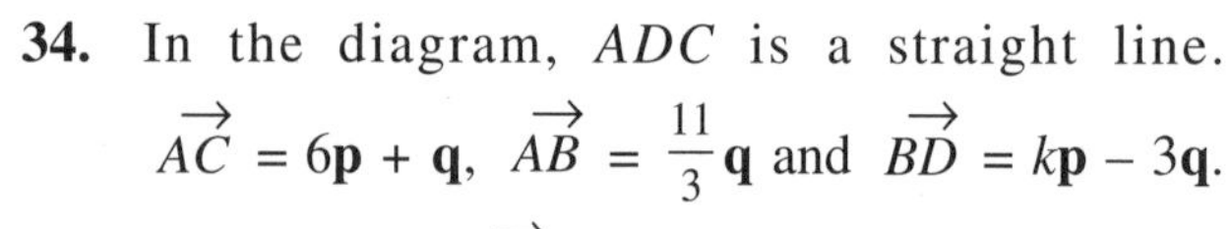

$\overrightarrow{AC} = 6\mathbf{p} + \mathbf{q}$, $\overrightarrow{AB} = \frac{11}{3}\mathbf{q}$ and $\overrightarrow{BD} = k\mathbf{p} - 3\mathbf{q}$.

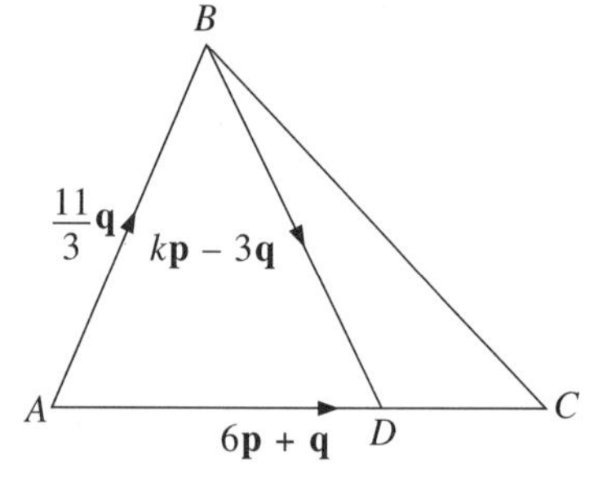

(a) Express $\overrightarrow{BC}$ in terms of $\mathbf{p}$ and $\mathbf{q}$.

(b) The point X outside $\triangle ABC$ is such that $\overrightarrow{AX} = 9\mathbf{p} - 4\mathbf{q}$. Is $\overrightarrow{AX}$ parallel to $\overrightarrow{BC}$? Justify your answer.

(c) Express $\overrightarrow{AD}$ in terms of $\mathbf{p}$, $\mathbf{q}$ and k.

(d) Given that $\overrightarrow{AD} = h\overrightarrow{AC}$, form an equation involving $\mathbf{p}$, $\mathbf{q}$, h and k and use it to find the value of h and of k.

(e) Hence express $\overrightarrow{BD}$ and $\overrightarrow{AD}$ in terms of $\mathbf{p}$ and $\mathbf{q}$ only.

35. In the figure, P divides OA in the ratio 2 : 1 and Q divides OB in the ratio 3 : 1.

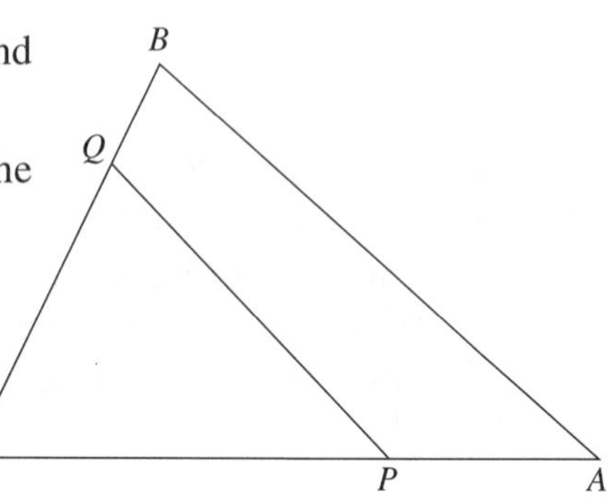

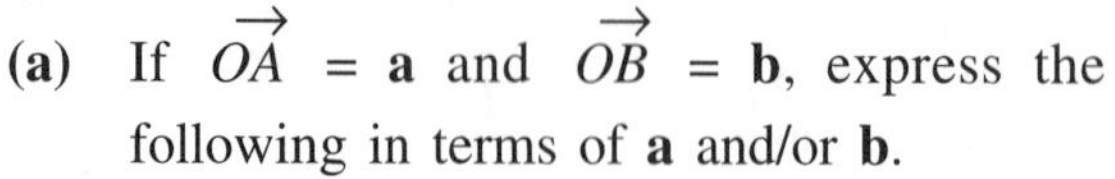

(a) If $\overrightarrow{OA} = \mathbf{a}$ and $\overrightarrow{OB} = \mathbf{b}$, express the following in terms of $\mathbf{a}$ and/or $\mathbf{b}$.

(i) $\overrightarrow{OP}$

(ii) $\overrightarrow{OQ}$

(c) Show that $12\overrightarrow{PQ} = 9\overrightarrow{OB} - 8\overrightarrow{OA}$.

TEST PAPER 1

Time : 1 hour
Marks : 50

*Answer all the questions **without** the use of a calculator.*

1. Construct the triangle PQR where PQ = 8.5 cm, QR = 6 cm and $P\hat{Q}R = 30°$. [2]

(a) Measure and write down the length of PR. [1]

(b) On the same diagram, and on the same side of PQ as R, construct the locus of points at which PQ subtends an angle of 60°. [2]

(c) Mark on the diagram a point X such that $\triangle PXQ$ is an equilateral triangle. [1]

Ans (a) ______________________

2. **(a)** Construct in a single diagram,

(i) triangle DEF with base DE = 5 cm, EF = 6 cm and DF = 7.5 cm, [1]

(ii) the point P such that $D\hat{P}E = 90°$ and P is equidistant from DE and DF, [1]

(iii) the point Q such that $\triangle DEQ$ is an isosceles triangle with $DE = EQ$ and D, P and Q lying on a straight line. [1]

(b) Hence, measure and write down

(i) the perpendicular distance from E to DQ, [1]

(ii) the size of $D\hat{E}Q$. [1]

Ans (b) (i) ____________________

(ii) ____________________

3. **(a)** Construct the parallelogram $ABCD$ in which $AB = 6$ cm, $AD = 4$ cm and $B\hat{A}D = 60°$. [2]

(b) On the same diagram, construct

(i) the locus of a point X which moves so that it is equidistant from B and D, [1]

(ii) the locus of a point Y which moves so that $B\hat{Y}D = 90°$, [1]

(iii) the locus of a point Z, on the same side of AB as C, which moves so that $\triangle ABZ = 6.6$ cm^2. [1]

(c) The point P, inside the parallelogram, is such that $B\hat{P}D \geqslant 90°$, area of $\triangle APB \geqslant 6.6$ cm^2 and $DP \geqslant BP$. Shade the region in which P must lie. [1]

4. XY is a fixed line segment 10 cm long.

(a) A point P is such that it is 6 cm from X. Describe the locus of P. [1]

(b) A point Q is such that $QY = 2$ cm. Describe the locus of Q. [1]

(c) A point R is such that $RX = RY$. Describe the locus of R. [1]

(d) Describe the set of points of intersection of

(i) the locus of P and of Q, [1]

(ii) the locus of Q and of R. [1]

Ans (a) ______________________

(b) ______________________

(c) ______________________

(d) (i) ______________________

(ii) ______________________

5.

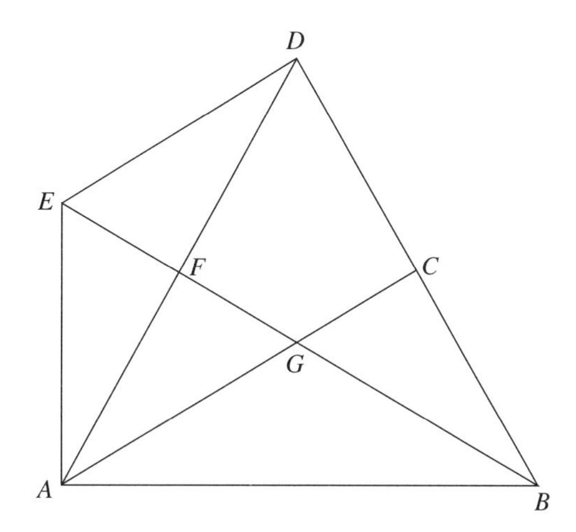

Using the diagram, complete the missing vectors in the following statements.

(a) $\overrightarrow{AE} = \overrightarrow{AD} +$ ______________ [1]

(b) $\overrightarrow{AC} = \overrightarrow{AE} +$ ______________ $+ \overrightarrow{BC}$ [1]

(c) $\overrightarrow{AC} = \overrightarrow{AE} + \overrightarrow{EB} +$ ______________ $+ \overrightarrow{DC}$ [1]

(d) $\overrightarrow{BE} =$ ______________ $+ \overrightarrow{AD} + \overrightarrow{DE}$ [1]

Ans (a) ____________________

(b) ____________________

(c) ____________________

(d) ____________________

6.

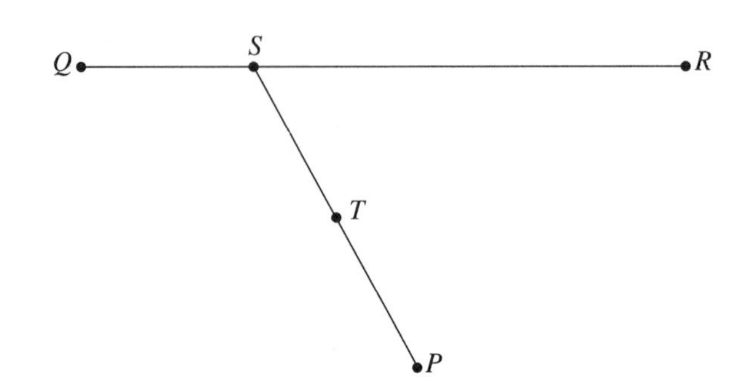

In the diagram, $\overrightarrow{PS} = \mathbf{a}$, $\overrightarrow{QR} = \mathbf{b}$, S and T are points such that $\overrightarrow{PS} = 2\overrightarrow{PT}$ and $\overrightarrow{QS} = \frac{2}{5}\overrightarrow{SR}$. Find the following in terms of **a** and **b**.

(a) $\overrightarrow{ST}$ [1]

(b) $\overrightarrow{SR}$ [1]

(c) $\overrightarrow{QT}$ [1]

(d) $\overrightarrow{PR}$ [1]

Ans (a) ______________________

(b) ______________________

(c) ______________________

(d) ______________________

7. **(a)** Given the vectors $\mathbf{a} = \begin{pmatrix} 1 \\ 1 \end{pmatrix}$ and $\mathbf{b} = \begin{pmatrix} 2 \\ -5 \end{pmatrix}$, find

(i) $2\mathbf{a} + \mathbf{b}$, [2]

(ii) $|2\mathbf{a} + \mathbf{b}|$. [2]

(b) Given that $\mathbf{c} = \begin{pmatrix} h \\ -6 \end{pmatrix}$ and $\mathbf{c}$ is parallel to $2\mathbf{a} + \mathbf{b}$, find the value of h. [1]

Ans (a) (i) ____________________

(ii) ____________________

(b) ____________________

8. Two points P and Q have position vectors **p** and **q** respectively, relative to the origin O.

Given that $\mathbf{p} = \begin{pmatrix} 3 \\ -4 \end{pmatrix}$ and $\mathbf{q} = \begin{pmatrix} 5 \\ 4 \end{pmatrix}$, find

(a) the position vector of $-3\mathbf{p} + 4\mathbf{q}$, [2]

(b) the coordinates of the point R where $\frac{1}{4}\overrightarrow{OQ} - \frac{1}{3}\overrightarrow{OR} = \frac{1}{2}\overrightarrow{OP}$. [2]

Ans (a) ____________________

(b) ____________________

9. The position vectors of the points A, B and C are **a**, **b** and **c** respectively. Find **c** in terms of **a** and **b** if

(a) $5\overrightarrow{AC} + \overrightarrow{CB} = 0$, [2]

(b) $2\overrightarrow{BC} = -3\overrightarrow{AC}$. [2]

Ans (a) ____________________

(b) ____________________

10.

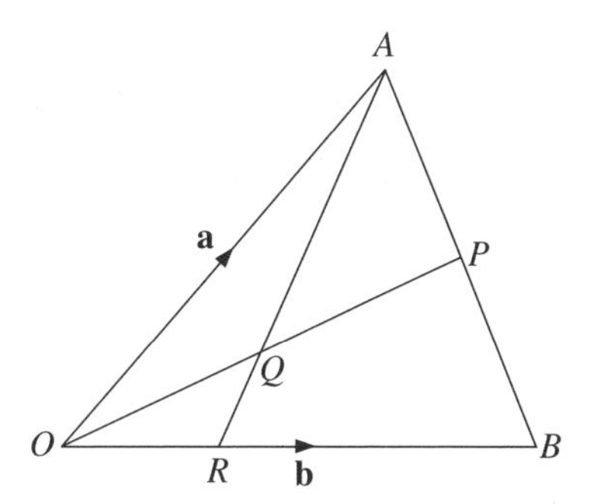

The position vectors of A and B referred to the origin O are $\mathbf{a}$ and $\mathbf{b}$ respectively. The point P is the midpoint of AB and Q is the midpoint of OP. The line AQ produced cuts OB at R.

(a) Find, in terms of $\mathbf{a}$ and $\mathbf{b}$,

(i) $\overrightarrow{OQ}$, [1]

(ii) $\overrightarrow{AQ}$. [1]

(b) Given that $\overrightarrow{AR} = h\overrightarrow{AQ}$ and $\overrightarrow{OR} = k\overrightarrow{OB}$, form an equation involving $\mathbf{a}$, $\mathbf{b}$, h and k, and hence solve for h and k. [3]

(c) Write down the numerical value of $\dfrac{OR}{RB}$. [2]

Ans (a) (i) ____________________

(ii) ____________________

(b) ____________________

(c) ____________________

CHAPTER 3 Transformations

1. Find the coordinates of the image of (3, –2) under each of the following transformations.
   (a) Reflection in the x-axis
   (b) Reflection in the line $y = -x$
   (c) Reflection in the line $y + 4 = 0$
   (d) Rotation through 90°, anticlockwise
   (e) Translation $\begin{pmatrix} -3 \\ 4 \end{pmatrix}$
   (f) Enlargement with centre at the origin and factor $1\frac{1}{2}$
   (g) Shear parallel to the y-axis with factor –4
   (h) Stretch parallel to the x-axis with factor $\frac{1}{3}$

2. In each case, find the coordinates of the point which will be mapped onto (7, 4) by the following transformations.
   (a) Reflection in the y-axis
   (b) Reflection in the line $y = x$
   (c) Reflection in the line $x = 2$
   (d) Rotation through 180° about (0, 0)
   (e) Translation $\begin{pmatrix} 2 \\ 5 \end{pmatrix}$
   (f) Enlargement with centre at the origin and factor –2
   (g) Shear parallel to the x-axis with factor 3
   (h) Stretch parallel to the y-axis with factor 2

3. In each case, describe completely the transformation which maps (2, 5) onto
   (a) (5, 2),
   (b) (2, –5),
   (c) (–5, 2),
   (d) (12, 5),
   (e) (4, 10).

4. A translation maps the point (0, 5) onto (5, –1).
   (a) Write down a column vector that defines the translation.
   (b) Under the same translation, find the image of
      (i) (–7, 0),
      (ii) (8, 9),
      (iii) $y = x - 4$.
   (c) Find the point whose image is
      (i) (5, –6),
      (ii) (1, 0),
      (iii) $y = 2x + 3$,
      under the same translation.

5. Find the image of
   (a) $(7, -2)$,
   (b) $y = 7x - 2$,
   (c) $x + y = 5$ under a reflection
      (i) in the x-axis,
      (ii) in the line $x + 3 = 0$.

6.

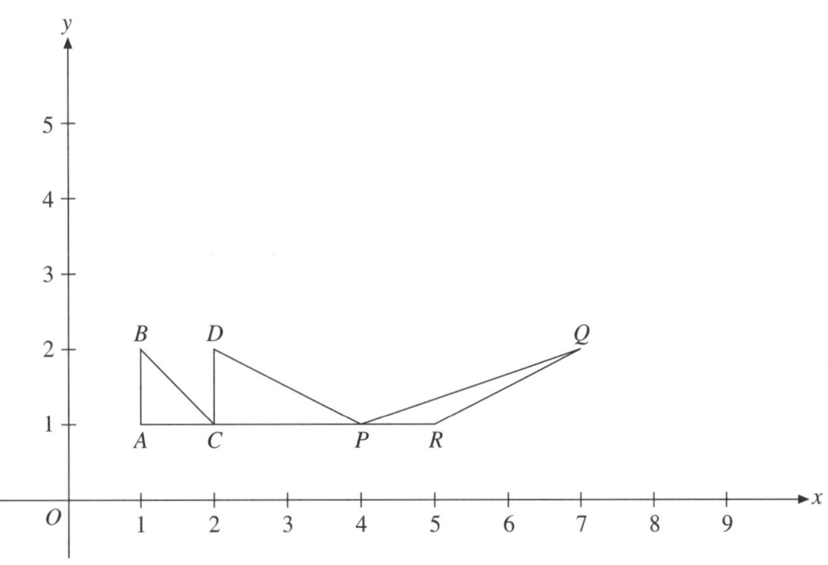

$\triangle ABC$ has vertices $A(1, 1)$, $B(1, 2)$ and $C(2, 1)$.
$\triangle PQR$ has vertices $P(4, 1)$, $Q(7, 2)$ and $R(5, 1)$.
$\triangle CDP$ has vertices $C(2, 1)$, $D(2, 2)$ and $P(4, 1)$.
The transformation U maps $\triangle ABC$ onto $\triangle PQR$.
The transformation V maps $\triangle ABC$ onto $\triangle CDP$.
   (a) Describe completely the transformations U and V.
   (b) Find the coordinates of the point whose image is $(2, -1)$ under U.
   (c) Find the coordinates of the image of $(2\frac{1}{2}, 6)$ under V.

7. In each of the following cases, describe completely the single transformation which maps $OABC$ onto
   (a) $OAQB$,
   (b) $OPQC$,
   (c) $PABQ$,
   (d) $APQB$,
   (e) $BAPQ$,
   (f) $QBAP$.

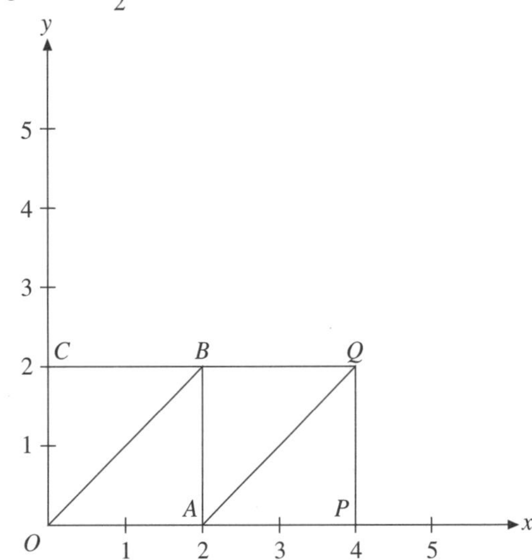

8.

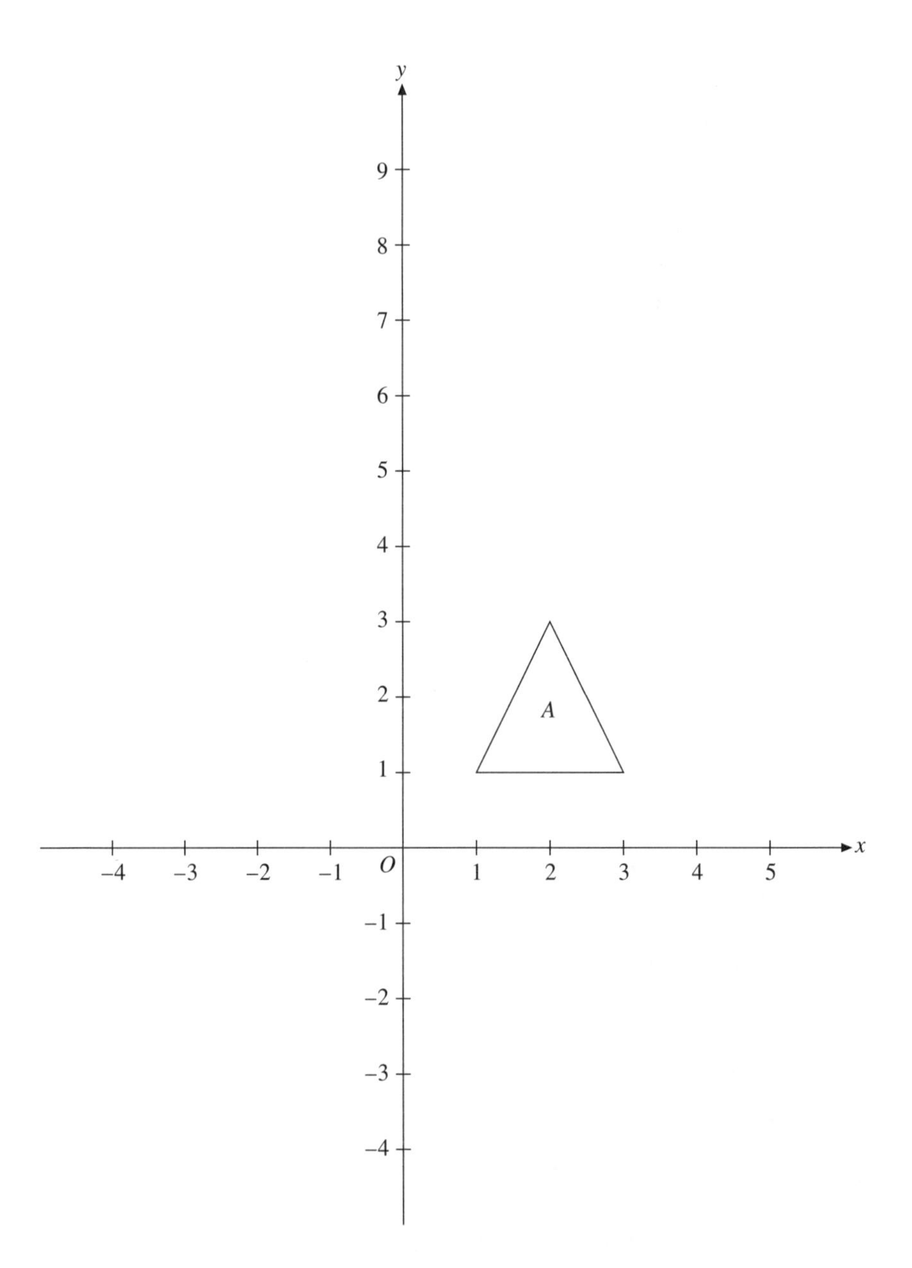

The diagram above shows the triangle A. Draw and label on the diagram,

(a) triangle B, the image of triangle A under a reflection in the line $y = -x$,

(b) triangle C, the image of triangle A under a clockwise rotation of 90° with centre (2, 0),

(c) triangle D, the image of triangle A under the translation $\begin{pmatrix} -2 \\ 3 \end{pmatrix}$.

9. M is a rotation through 90°, clockwise about the origin. Find the coordinates of the image of (3, –2) under

(a) M, **(b)** M^2, **(c)** M^4, **(d)** M^{21}.

10.

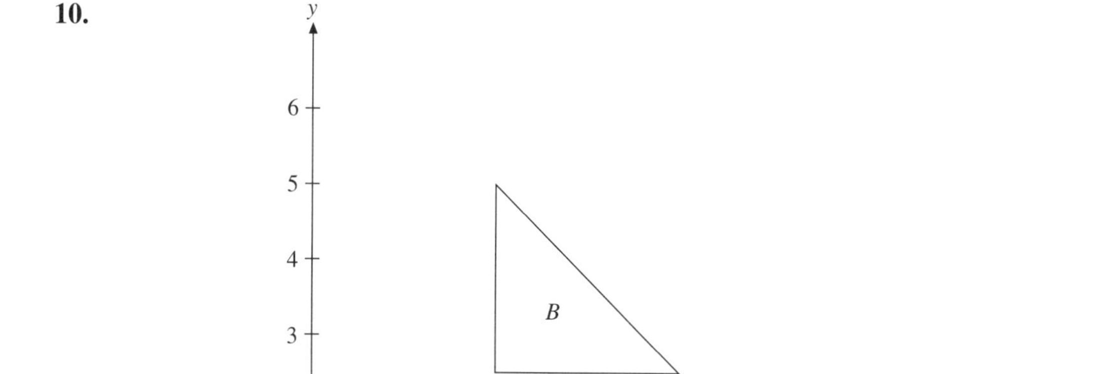

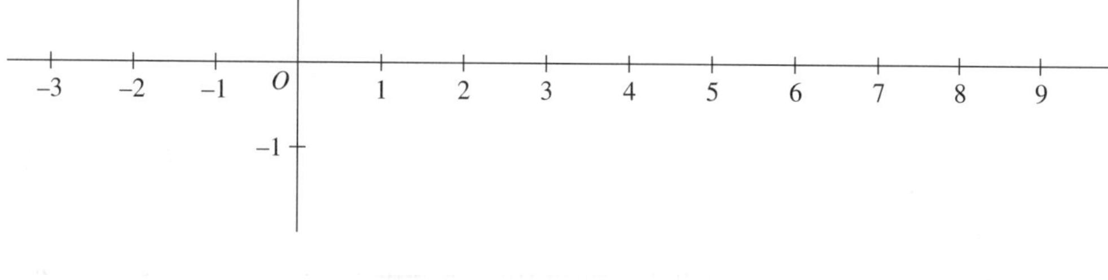

(a) Describe the transformation that maps triangle A onto
(i) triangle B, **(ii)** triangle C, **(iii)** triangle D.

(b) The transformation M is a reflection in the line $x = -1$. On the diagram, draw and label the triangle M(A).

(c) The transformation S is a one-way stretch parallel to the y-axis, with the x-axis invariant and with scale factor 3. On the diagram, draw and label S(A).

11. The vertices of $\triangle ABC$ are $A(1, 1)$, $B(3, 1)$ and $C(1, 2)$.

(a) Using a scale of 2 cm to represent 1 unit on each axis, draw x and y axes for $-3 \leqslant x \leqslant 6$ and $-3 \leqslant y \leqslant 7$. Draw and label $\triangle ABC$.

(b) The transformation Y maps $\triangle ABC$ onto $\triangle PQR$ where P is $(-2, 4)$, Q is $(-2, 6)$ and R is $(-3, 4)$.
(i) Draw and label $\triangle PQR$.
(ii) Describe fully the transformation Y.

12. The unit square $ABCD$ has vertices $(1, 1)$, $(1, 2)$, $(0, 2)$ and $(0, 1)$.

(a) The square $ABCD$ is mapped onto the square $A_1B_1C_1D_1$ by an enlargement, centre O, such that C_1 is the point $(0, -6)$. Find
(i) the scale factor of the enlargement,
(ii) the coordinates of B_1.

(b) The square $ABCD$ is mapped onto the square $A_2B_2C_2D_2$ by a reflection in the y-axis, followed by a reflection in the line $x = -4$. Find the coordinates of A_2.

(c) Find the value of the ratio $\dfrac{\text{area of } A_1B_1C_1D_1}{\text{area of } A_2B_2C_2D_2}$.

13.

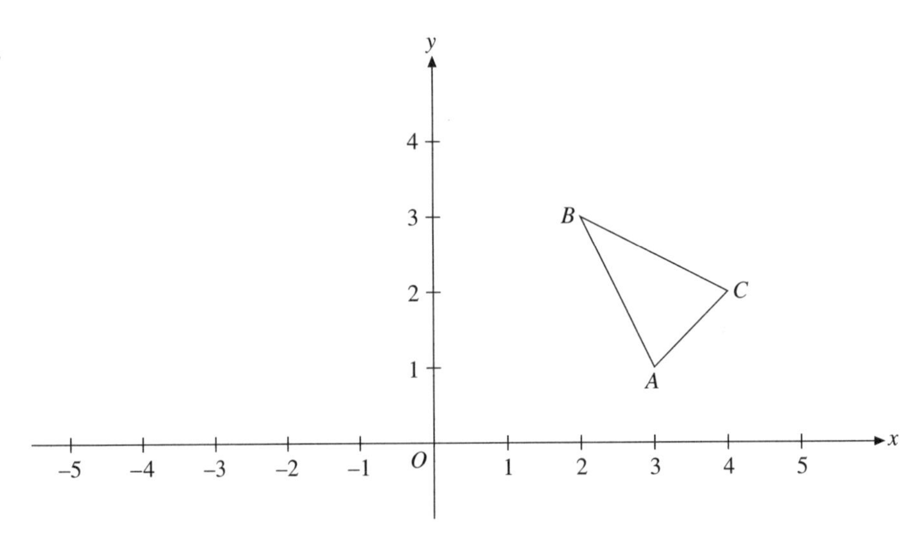

The triangle ABC has vertices $A(3, 1)$, $B(2, 3)$ and $C(4, 2)$.

(a) Draw, on the diagram, the image of the triangle ABC under

(i) an anticlockwise rotation of 90° about the origin O, labelling the image $\triangle PQR$,

(ii) a reflection in the line $x + y = 0$, labelling the image $\triangle XYZ$.

(b) Describe completely a single transformation which maps $\triangle ABC$ onto $\triangle XYZ$.

14. T is the translation $\begin{pmatrix} 8 \\ -4 \end{pmatrix}$ and R is an anticlockwise rotation of 90° about the origin.

A is the point (2, 0), B is (4, 4), C is (8, –2) and D is (–3, –5). Find the coordinates of

(a) R(A),

(b) P, if T(P) = B,

(c) RT(C),

(d) Q if TR(Q) = D.

15. ABC is a triangle whose vertices are $A(2, 2)$, $B(5, 3)$ and $C(3, 5)$.

(a) An anticlockwise rotation of 90° with centre B maps C onto the point D. Find the coordinates of D.

(b) An enlargement with centre (0, 3) maps $\triangle ABC$ onto $\triangle EFG$. Given that E is a point on the x-axis, write down

(i) the coordinates of E,

(ii) the scale factor of the enlargement,

(iii) the coordinates of the point F.

(c) A shear, with the y-axis as invariant line, maps $\triangle ABC$ onto $\triangle PQR$, where Q is the point (5, 4).

(i) Find the coordinates of R.

(ii) Write down the numerical value of $\dfrac{\text{area of } \triangle PQR}{\text{area of } \triangle EFG}$.

16. **(a)** The point $P(-2, 7)$ is rotated clockwise through 90° about the origin onto the point P_1. Write down the coordinates of P_1.

(b) The line $y = \frac{x}{2} - 3$ is mapped onto the line l by a reflection in the x-axis. Find the equation of l.

(c) An enlargement, centre at the origin, maps (4, 6) onto (10, 15). Find

(i) the scale factor of the enlargement,

(ii) the image of the point (5, 1) under the enlargement.

17. Describe the transformation which maps triangle X onto

(a) triangle A,

(b) triangle B,

(c) triangle C,

(d) triangle D,

(e) triangle E.

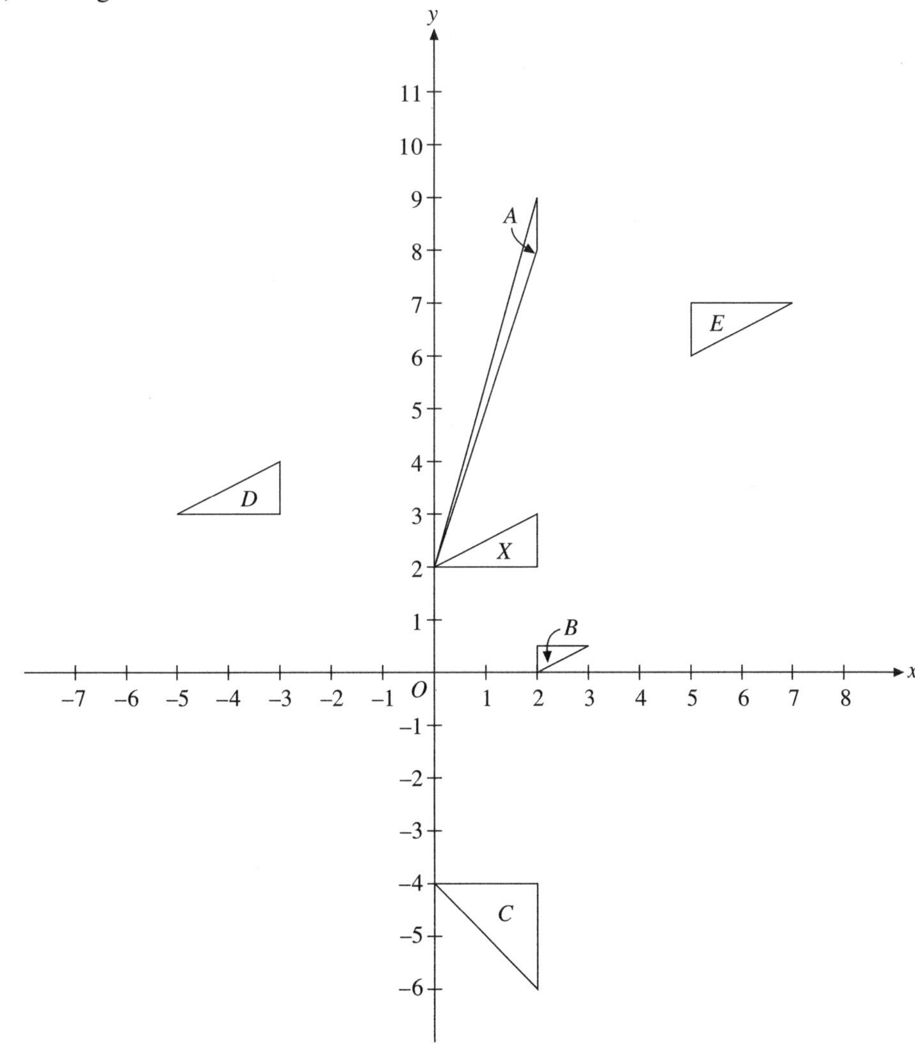

18.

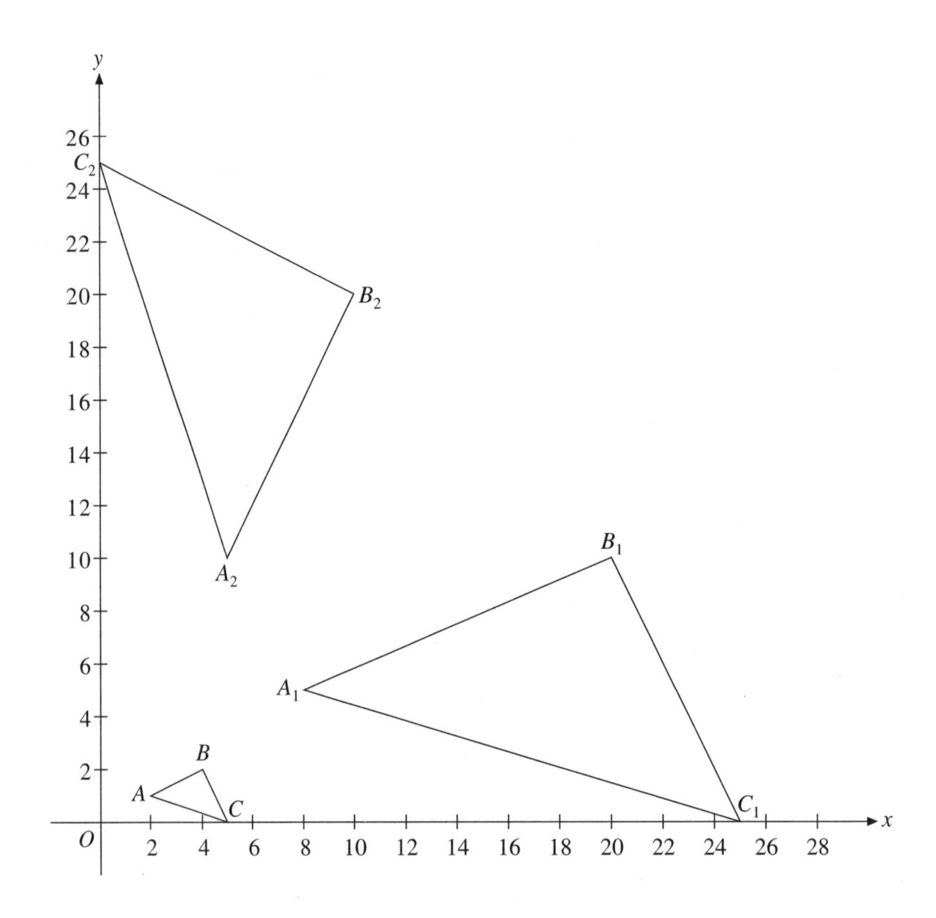

Describe the transformation that maps

(a) $\triangle ABC$ onto $\triangle A_1B_1C_1$,

(b) $\triangle A_1B_1C_1$ onto $\triangle A_2B_2C_2$.

CHAPTER 4 Probability

1. A bag contains 40 discs of which 16 are black and 24 are white. Find the probability that if a disc is picked at random, it will be a black one.

2. A box contains 6 red pens and 9 blue pens. If one pen is withdrawn at random, what is the chance that it is not a red pen?

3. One integer is chosen from the numbers, 2, 3, 7, 8, 10, 11, 12, 15. What is the probability that it is
   (a) a prime number,
   (b) a number which is divisible by either 2 or 5,
   (c) a number which is divisible by both 2 and 3?

4. What is the chance of getting a 'head' when
   (a) an unbiased coin is tossed,
   (b) two unbiased coins are tossed,
   (c) three unbiased coins are tossed?

5. A card is picked at random from 10 cards numbered 1, 2, 3, . . . , 10. Find the probability that the card picked
   (a) is not divisible by 4,
   (b) is a square number,
   (c) is a prime number.

6. A fair dice is rolled. Find the probability that the score is
   (a) a '6',
   (b) an even number or an odd number,
   (c) less than 3.

7. One card is drawn from a pack of 52 playing cards. What is the chance of getting
   (a) an ace,
   (b) a diamond,
   (c) an ace or a king,
   (d) a spade which is not an ace,
   (e) a ten, jack, queen or king of hearts?

8. What is the probability that an arrangement of the letters of the word TELEVISION begins with the letter
   (a) V, **(b)** E, **(c)** N or I?

9. Two fair dice are thrown. Find the probability that the total score is
   (a) '6',
   (b) not more than 4.

10. Two cards are drawn from a pack of 52 playing cards. What is the probability of getting
(a) 2 aces, **(b)** an ace and a king, **(c)** at least one ace?

11. There are 3 black balls and 4 red balls in a bag. If two balls are drawn one after another without replacement, find the probability that
(a) both are of the same colour,
(b) at least one is red.

12. A boy throws a dice, tosses a coin and picks a card at random from a pack of 52 playing cards. What is the probability that he gets a six, a head and an ace?

13. There are 28 books on a shelf of which 20 are paperbacks and 8 are hardbacks.
(a) A book is taken at random from the shelf. What is the probability that it is a paperback?
(b) Two books are taken at random from the shelf. What is the probability that
(i) both are paperbacks,
(ii) at least one is a hardback?

14. The chances of 3 boys winning a prize are $\frac{1}{3}$, $\frac{3}{4}$ and $\frac{2}{5}$. Calculate the probability that
(a) all win, **(b)** all lose,
(c) only one wins, **(d)** at least one wins.

15. There are 2 tins of coloured biscuits.
Tin A contains 2 brown and 3 red biscuits.
Tin B contains 5 brown and 3 red biscuits.
If one biscuit is drawn from each tin, find the probability that
(a) only one is brown, **(b)** neither is brown.

16. The diagram shows a spinner consisting of 4 coloured sectors.
(a) If the pointer is spun once, find the probability that
(i) it stops on the blue sector,
(ii) it stops on either the green or the red sector.
(b) If the pointer is spun twice, find the probability that
(i) it stops on the yellow sector in both spins,
(ii) it stops on the green sector in the first spin and on the yellow sector in the second spin,
(iii) it stops on the yellow sector in the second spin.

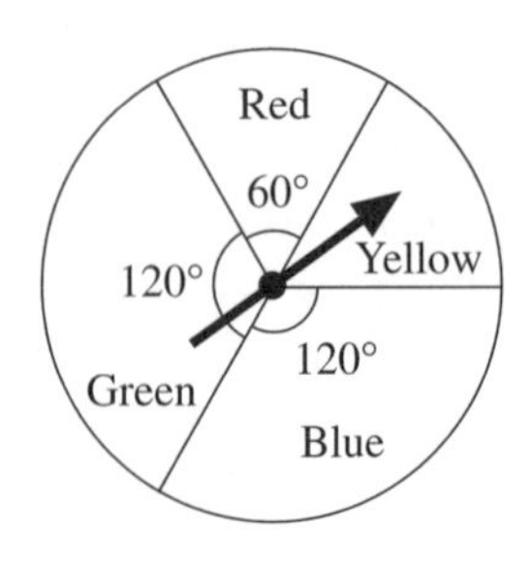

17. A fair dice is rolled.
(a) What is the probability of getting a ‘5’?
(b) Estimate the number of times that a ‘5’ is obtained when the dice is rolled 60 times.

18. Two coins are tossed.

(a) Find the probability of getting 2 heads.

(b) Estimate the number of times of getting 2 heads when the coins are tossed 48 times.

19. In a survey, it is found that the probability of a family having 4 children is $\frac{1}{8}$. Calculate the number of families involved in the survey if it is found that 50 families have 4 children.

20. In the multiple-choice section of an examination, each question has 3 possible answers, only one of which is correct. If a candidate chooses his answers at random, find the probability that

(a) he answers a question correctly,

(b) out of 10 questions, he gets none correct.

21. The probability of an archer hitting the bull's-eye with any one shot is $\frac{2}{5}$. Find the probability that in three successive shots, he hits the bull's-eye exactly once.

22. A housewife has nine 10¢ coins, five 20¢ coins and one 50¢ coin in her purse. She takes two coins at random from her purse one after the other. The tree diagram below shows the possible outcomes and some of the probabilities.

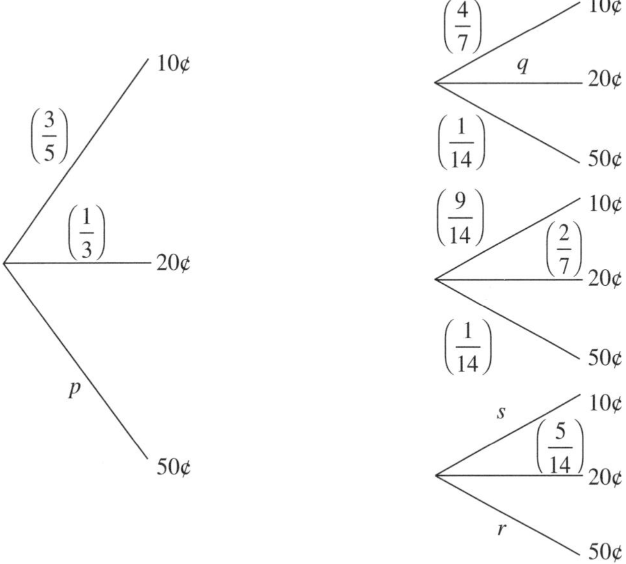

(a) Find the values of p, q, r and s.

(b) Find the probability that the total value of the two coins taken out is

(i) 40¢, **(ii)** \$1, **(iii)** 70¢.

23. Two bags A and B each contains a complete set of the 26 letters of the alphabet.

(a) If one letter is selected at random from bag A, write down the probability that it is a vowel.

(b) If one letter is selected from each bag, calculate the probability that both letters are the letter 'T'.

24. Six cards each have a single digit written on them. The digits are '1', '2', '4', '5', '7' and '9'.

(a) One card is chosen at random. Find the probability that it is the card with digit '4'.

(b) Two cards are chosen at random. Find the probability that

(i) the digit on each card is odd,

(ii) the digits on these two cards add up to 11,

(iii) the difference between the digits on these two cards is more than 5.

25. A box contains 6 green balls and 10 red balls.

(a) A ball is drawn at random from the box. What is the probability that the ball is red?

(b) Two balls are drawn at random and without replacement. Calculate the probability that

(i) both are green,

(ii) one is green and one is red.

(c) x yellow balls are added into the box. Then, after thoroughly mixing them up, a ball is drawn from the box.

(i) Write down, in terms of x, an expression for the probability that the ball drawn is yellow.

(ii) Given that this probability is $\frac{3}{7}$, find x.

26. I have a choice of two routes to get to work. The probability that I choose the first route to get to work on any day is $\frac{3}{5}$, and the probabilities of my being delayed on the journey are $\frac{1}{20}$ for the first route and $\frac{1}{10}$ for the second.

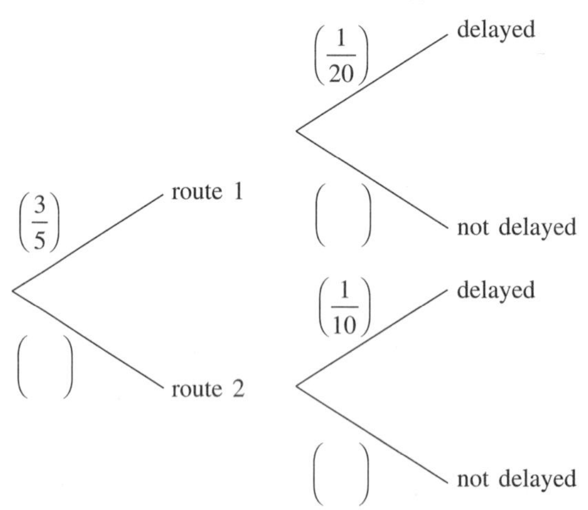

(a) Complete the probability tree diagram.

(b) Find the probability that

(i) I get to work on the first route and I am delayed,

(ii) I get to work without being delayed.

(c) In a certain week, I worked only 2 days. Find the probability that I was delayed once in the 2 days.

27. A bag contains 4 white and 6 red discs. One disc is drawn at random. If it is white, it is replaced in the bag, but if it is red, it is not replaced. A second disc is then drawn.

(a) Complete the probability tree diagram.

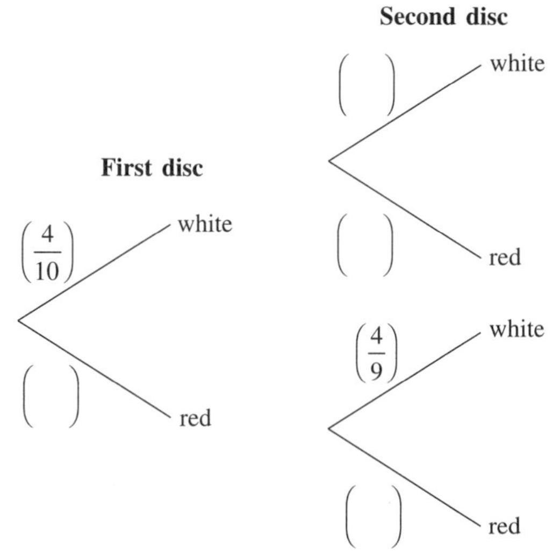

(b) Find the probability that
- **(i)** both discs are white,
- **(ii)** the second disc is red given that the first disc is red,
- **(iii)** the second disc is white,
- **(iv)** either the first disc is red or the second disc is red, but not both.

28. An unbiased six-sided dice is thrown twice.

(a) Find the probability that
- **(i)** the total score is 8,
- **(ii)** both the scores are different.

(b) If the two scores are multiplied together, complete the table to show all the possible outcomes.

(c) Hence, find the probability that
- **(i)** the product is an odd number,
- **(ii)** the product is at least 20.

×	**1**	**2**	**3**	**4**	**5**	**6**
1	1	2	3	4	5	6
2	2	4				
3		6	9	12	15	18
4		8		16		
5		10		20	25	30
6		12		24		

29. A regular tetrahedron, which has its four triangular faces numbered 1 to 4, is to be used as a dice.

(a) If it is thrown twice, show all the possible outcomes of the total score.

(b) Find the probability that
- **(i)** the score in the first throw is either 2 or 3,
- **(ii)** each throw shows a score of 4,
- **(iii)** the total score does not exceed 5,
- **(iv)** the scores in both throws are odd.

30. A regular octahedron, which has its eight triangular faces numbered 1 to 8, is used as a dice. If it is thrown twice, find the probability that
(a) a '6' appears in the first throw,
(b) a '3' appears in the first throw and a '7' appears in the second throw,
(c) the score in the first throw is twice the score in the second throw,
(d) the total score is at least 14.

31. Two six-sided unbiased dice are thrown together. Find the probability that
(a) the total score is 12,
(b) the difference between the scores is 2,
(c) either the score on one dice is 1 or the score on the other dice is 6, but not both,
(d) each dice scores at least 5 points.

32. $ABCD$ is a square and P, Q and R are the midpoints of the sides AB, AD and CD respectively.
(a) A point is selected at random in the square. Calculate the probability that it lies in
(i) the triangle APQ,
(ii) the triangle BCR.
(b) Two points are selected at random in the square. Calculate the probability that both points lie in the unshaded region.
(c) Given that the area of the unshaded region is 90 cm^2, find the perimeter of the square $ABCD$.

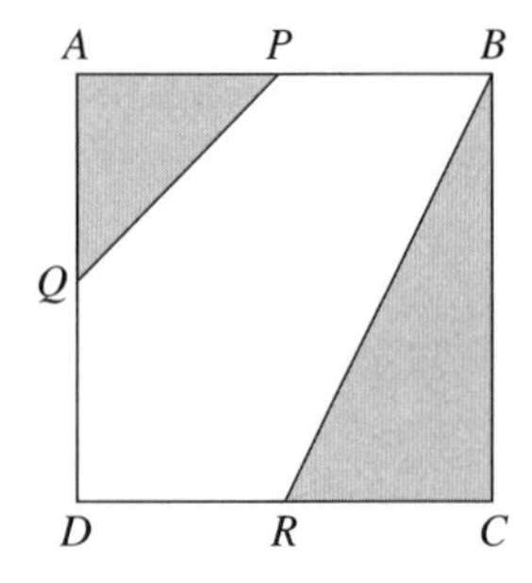

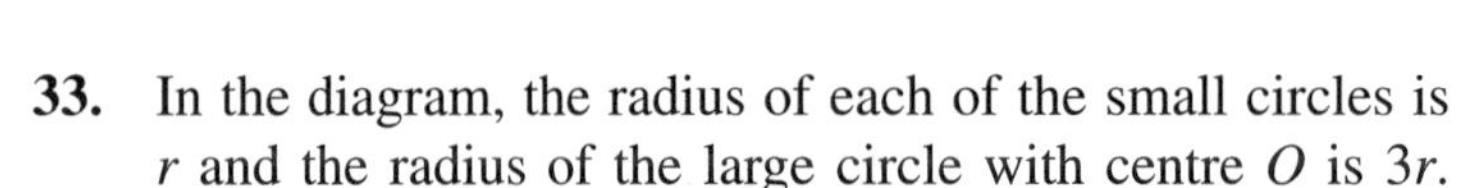

33. In the diagram, the radius of each of the small circles is r and the radius of the large circle with centre O is $3r$.
(a) Write down, in terms of π, the area of a small circle and the area of the large circle.
(b) A point is selected at random in the large circle.
(i) Find the probability that it lies in the small circle with centre O.
(ii) Find the probability that it lies in the shaded region.

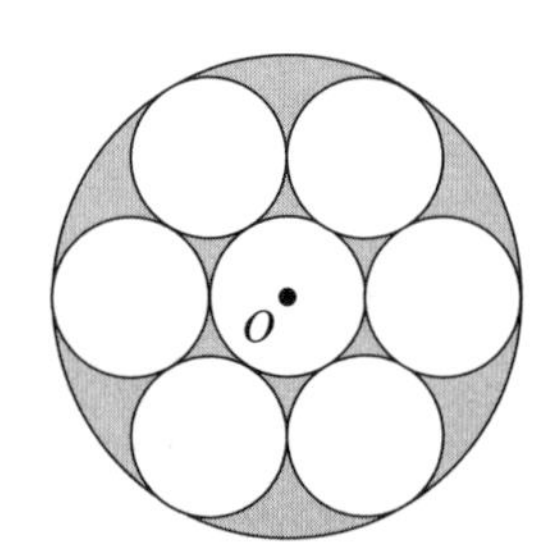

34. The diagram represents a target consisting of two concentric circles of radii 2 cm and 3 cm. A player hits the target every time he throws a dart and is equally likely to hit any part of the target.
(a) A dart is thrown. Find the probability that it will hit the target on the unshaded area.
(b) Three darts were thrown. Find the probability that
(i) all three darts landed on the shaded area,
(ii) two darts landed on the shaded area and one on the unshaded area.

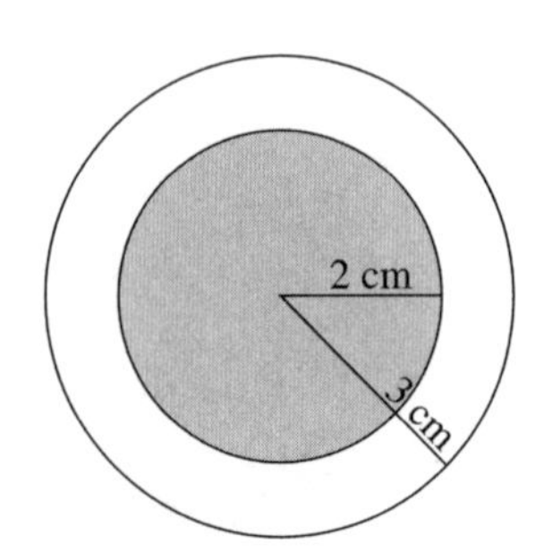

35.

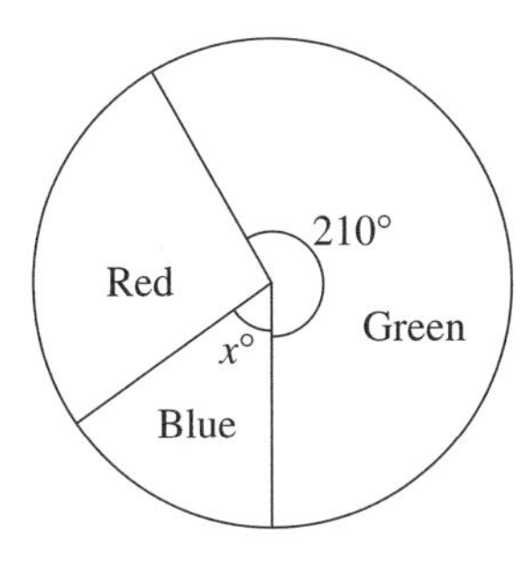

The diagram shows a rotary board consisting of three coloured sectors. A ball bearing is placed on the board. After the board is rotated and stopped, the ball bearing will come to rest at random on either the red, the green, or the blue sector of the board.

(a) Given that the probability that the ball bearing will come to rest on the blue sector is $\frac{3}{20}$, find

(i) the value of x,

(ii) the probability that it will rest on the green sector,

(iii) the probability that it will rest on the red sector.

(b) A player scores 3 points, 2 points and 1 point respectively when the ball bearing comes to rest on the blue, red and green sectors.

(i) The board is rotated once. Find the probability that the player will score 3 points.

(ii) The board is rotated twice. Find the probability that the player will score a total of 4 points.

36. An experiment is carried out with two coins. One of the coins is fair, so that the probability of obtaining a 'head' on any throw is $\frac{1}{2}$. The other coin is biased, so that the probability of obtaining a 'head' on any throw is $\frac{1}{4}$. The two coins are thrown. Find the probability that

(a) only 1 head is obtained,

(b) both coins show the same result.

37. Three fair coins are thrown simultaneously. Find the probability that

(a) only 1 head is obtained,

(b) 3 heads are obtained.

38. An unbiased six-sided dice has the number '1' on one face, the number '2' on two faces and the number '3' on three faces.

(a) The dice is rolled once, find the probability of scoring '2'.

(b) The dice is rolled twice, find the probability of scoring

(i) a total of 3, **(ii)** a total of 4.

39. A bag contains 5 white balls and 3 red balls. Two balls are drawn from the bag at random. Find the probability that the balls drawn are

(a) of different colours,

(b) both white.

40. A box contains 20 apples, of which 15 are red and 5 are green. Of the red apples, 3 are bruised, and of the green apples, 1 is bruised. An apple is chosen at random. Find the probability of getting

(a) a red apple,

(b) a green apple that is not bruised,

(c) an apple that is bruised.

41. A bag contains 12 red and 3 black counters. One counter is drawn at random.

(a) Write down the probability that the counter is black.

(b) A second counter is then drawn at random from the remaining 14 counters. Calculate the probability that

(i) the second counter is red given that the first counter is black,

(ii) both are red,

(iii) both are black,

(iv) they are of different colours.

42. **(a)** There are x fishes in a tank, of which 25 are of species A and the rest are of species B. One fish is selected at random. Find the value of x, given that the probability that the fish selected is of species B is $\frac{1}{6}$.

(b) In another tank, there are 27 fishes of species A and 13 fishes of species B. Two fishes are selected at random. Calculate the probability that

(i) both are of species A,

(ii) both are of different species.

43. Two boxes each contains 8 cards. In each box, there are 5 red cards, 2 blue cards and 1 yellow card.

(a) One card is drawn at random from the first box. Find the probability that it is not red.

(b) Two cards are drawn at random from the second box. Find the probability that

(i) they are not blue,

(ii) at least one card is blue.

(c) All the cards are now returned to their original boxes. One card is drawn from each box. Find the probability that the two cards are

(i) both red,

(ii) each of a different colour.

44. Ben has 12 sweets in a can of which 5 are orange, 6 are purple and 1 is red. He takes 2 sweets at random from the can one after another.

(a) Complete the tree diagram below.

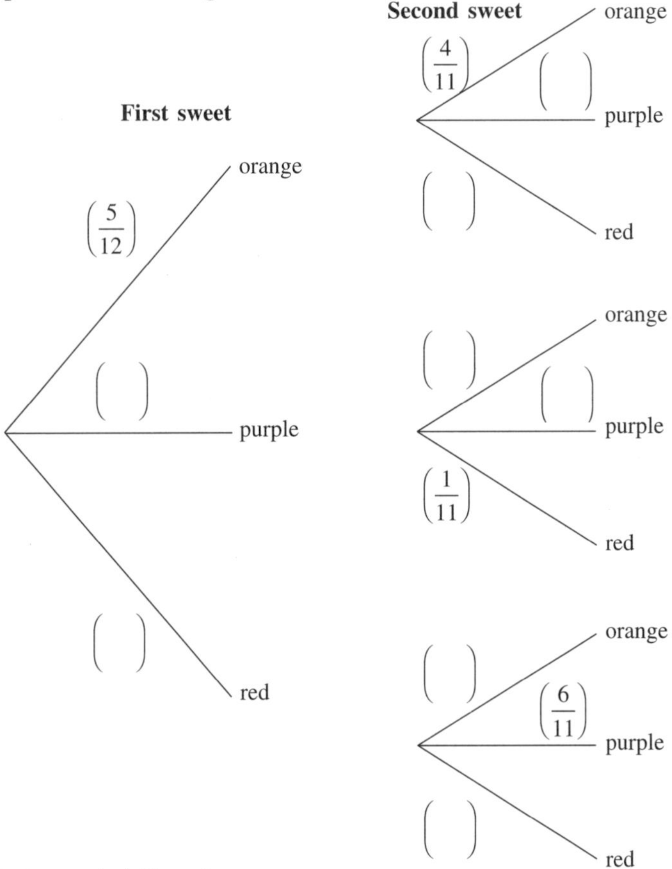

(b) Find the probability that

(i) both sweets are orange,

(ii) both sweets have different colours,

(iii) the first sweet is red and the second is purple,

(iv) the second sweet is orange.

(c) Ben then takes a third sweet. Find the probability that the third sweet is red.

45. There are 2 boxes of coloured balls. Box A contains 3 red balls, 4 white balls and 1 green ball. Box B contains 5 white balls and 3 green balls.

(a) One ball is drawn at random from box A. Find the probability that it is red.

(b) Two balls are drawn from box B. Find the probability that they are of the same colour.

(c) All the balls are now returned to their original boxes. One ball is drawn from each box. Find the probability that

(i) one is red and one is white,

(ii) one is white and one is green,

(iii) both are green,

(iv) both are red.

TEST PAPER 2

Time : 1 hour
Marks : 50

Answer all the questions ***without*** *the use of a calculator.*

1. T is a translation which maps the point (3, 5) onto the point (5, 7). If B' is the image of $B(x, y)$ under T, write down the coordinates of B' in terms of x and y. [2]

Ans ______________________

2. Find in terms of x and y, the image of $P(x, y)$ under each of the following transformations.

(a) Enlargement with centre as the origin and with factor

(i) $\frac{1}{2}$ **(ii)** $\frac{3}{4}$ [2]

(b) Shear with the y-axis as the invariant line and with factor

(i) 3 **(ii)** $-\frac{1}{3}$ [2]

(c) Stretching with the x-axis as the invariant line and with factor

(i) $1\frac{2}{3}$ **(ii)** 4 [2]

Ans (a) (i) ______________________

(ii) ______________________

(b) (i) ______________________

(ii) ______________________

(c) (i) ______________________

(ii) ______________________

3.

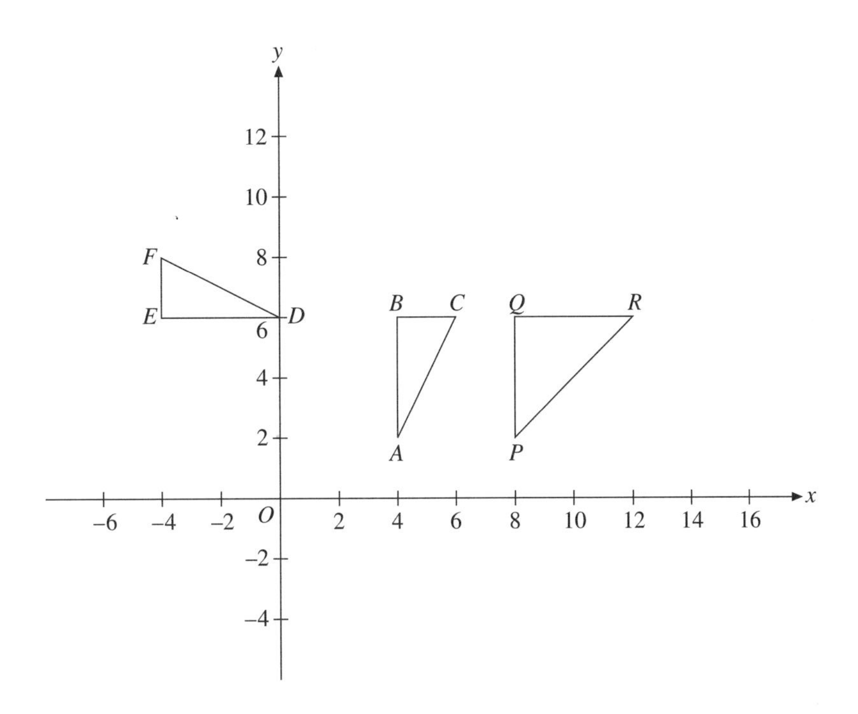

(a) Describe fully the single transformation which maps $\triangle ABC$ onto $\triangle DEF$. [2]

(b) $\triangle ABC$ is mapped onto $\triangle PQR$ by a stretch.

(i) Write down the equation of the invariant line. [1]

(ii) A point T is mapped onto the point (11, 4) by the stretch. Find the coordinates of T. [2]

Ans (a) ____________________

(b) (i) ____________________

(ii) ____________________

4. Answer this question on a sheet of graph paper.
The vertices of triangle ABC are $A(1, 2)$, $B(1, 3)$ and $C(2, 2)$.
The vertices of triangle $A_1B_1C_1$ are $A_1(4, 3)$, $B_1(4, 4)$ and $C_1(5, 3)$.

(a) Using a scale of 2 cm to represent 1 unit on each axis, draw x and y axes for $0 \leqslant x \leqslant 7$ and $-3 \leqslant y \leqslant 4$. Draw and label $\triangle ABC$ and $\triangle A_1B_1C_1$. [2]

(b) Describe fully the single transformation which maps $\triangle ABC$ onto $\triangle A_1B_1C_1$. [1]

(c) A reflection in the x-axis maps $\triangle ABC$ onto $\triangle A_2B_2C_2$. Draw and label $\triangle A_2B_2C_2$. [2]

Ans (b) ____________________

5. A bag contains 4 silver rings and 6 gold rings. Three rings are drawn at random from the bag without replacement. Calculate the probability that

(a) all the rings drawn are silver, [2]

(b) at least one ring of each colour is drawn, [3]

(c) at least two silver rings are drawn. [2]

Ans (a) ____________________

(b) ____________________

(c) ____________________

6. A game is played with an unbiased six-sided dice. The dice is thrown and if the result is 2, 3, 4 or 5, that result will be the player's score. If the result is 1 or 6, the dice is thrown a second time and the sum of the two numbers obtained from both throws will be the player's score. Find the probability that the player's score is

(a) 11, [2]

(b) 7, [2]

(c) 4. [2]

Ans (a) ____________________

(b) ____________________

(c) ____________________

7. **(a)** The probability that a netball team will not win in any particular game is $\frac{7}{12}$.

Find the probability that in the first two games of the season,

(i) the team will win one of the two games, [2]

(ii) the team will win both games. [1]

(b) The probability that the team will draw any particular game is $\frac{1}{9}$. Find the probability that the team will win the last game of the season. [2]

Ans (a) (i) ____________________

(ii) ____________________

(b) ____________________

8.

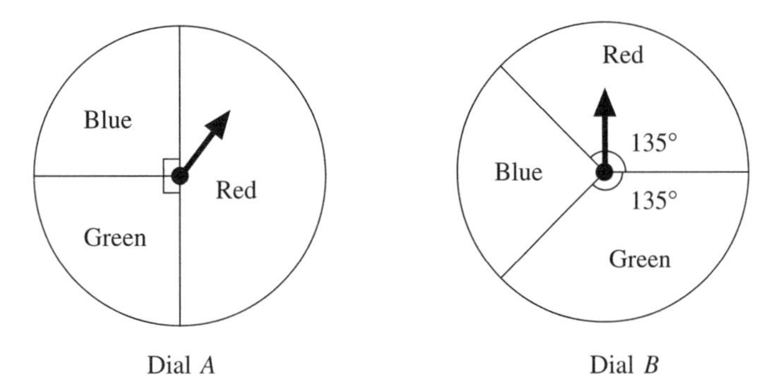

Dial A Dial B

The diagram shows two coloured dials A and B, each with a pointer pivoted at its centre. After being set in motion, the pointers come to rest independently in random positions. Find the probability that

(a) the pointers stop at the red sector of each dial, [2]

(b) the pointers point to the green sector of only one of the dials. [2]

Ans (a) ______________________

(b) ______________________

9. In a simple model of the weather chart, each day is classified as either fine or rainy. The probability that a certain day is fine is 0.6. The probability that a fine day is followed by a fine day is 0.7. The probability that a rainy day is followed by a fine day is 0.8.

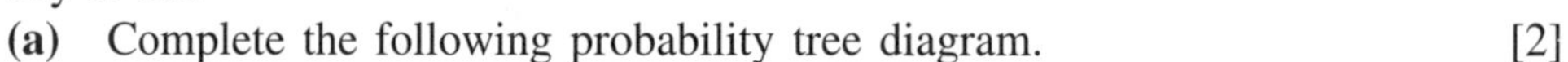

(a) Complete the following probability tree diagram. [2]

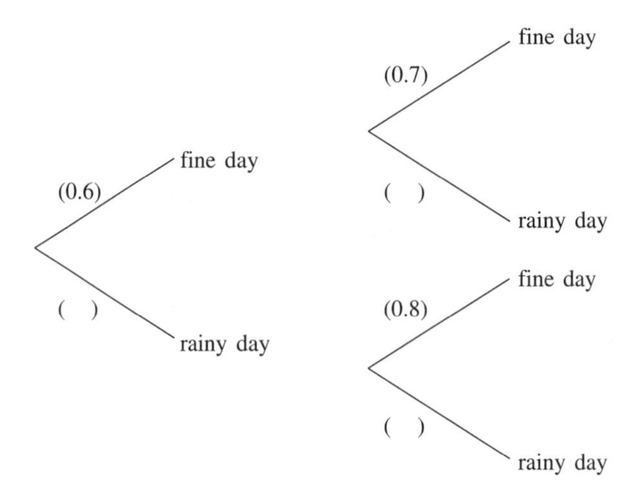

(b) Two days in June were observed. Find the probability that

(i) there is fine weather on both days, [1]

(ii) only one day is fine. [2]

Ans (b) (i) ____________________

(ii) ____________________

10. On any day, the probability that James will drink a cup of tea is $\frac{1}{4}$ and the probability that he will drink a cup of coffee is $\frac{5}{6}$.

(a) Find the probability that, on one particular day, James will not drink a cup of tea. [1]

(b) Find the probability that James will drink a cup of tea on just one of two particular consecutive days. [2]

(c) Find the probability that, on three consecutive days, James will drink a cup of coffee each day. [2]

Ans (a) ____________________

(b) ____________________

(c) ____________________

CHAPTER 5 Revision

5.1 Arithmetic

1. Evaluate

(a) $2\frac{2}{3} \times \frac{3}{4}$, **(b)** $3\frac{2}{5} + \frac{7}{10}$.

2. Calculate the exact value of

(a) 0.3×0.4, **(b)** $\sqrt{0.001\,6}$, **(c)** $15.2 - 17.5$.

3. A train arrived at a station at 20 06, it took 7 hours 35 mins. Find the time at which the train started its journey.

4. Given that $y = m\sqrt{x}$, where m is a constant, and that $y = 8$ when $x = 4$, find

(a) the value of m,

(b) the value of y when $x = 25$,

(c) the value of x when $y = 32$.

5. Mrs Yong buys an article marked at $340.00, but in addition, has to pay 15% tax. Calculate the total amount that she has to pay.

6. Given that $5 \leqslant x \leqslant 13$ and that $-1 \leqslant y \leqslant 4$, find the smallest and largest possible values of

(a) xy, **(b)** $\frac{x}{y}$.

7. A sum of money is divided among three sisters in the ratio 2 : 3 : 7. Given that the largest share is $700, calculate the smallest share.

8. 1 650 pupils go to a certain school and the way in which they travel to school is shown in the table below. No other form of transport is used.

Walk	x
Train	315
Bus	966
Car	240

(a) Calculate the value of x.

(b) Find the percentage of pupils who travel to school by bus.

(c) Of the pupils who travel to school by train, the ratio of boys to girls is 4 : 5. Calculate the number of girls who go to school by train.

9. In a cinema, there are 25 rows with 20 seats in each row. Seats in the first ten rows are priced at \$8.00 each and those in the other rows are priced at \$7.00 each.
   (a) Find the maximum possible taking.
   (b) At one show, there were 150 people in the \$8.00 seats and 215 people in the \$7.00 seats.
      (i) Write down the attendance, in fraction, of the maximum possible attendance.
      (ii) Calculate the amount of money paid for the seats at this show.
      (iii) Express this amount as a percentage of the maximum possible takings.
   (c) At one particular show, children were allowed in the \$7.00 seats only and were charged half price. The cinema was full and the takings were \$3 427. Calculate the number of children present.

10. The table below shows a series of odd numbers, the number of terms (n) in the series and the sum of the series (S).

Series	No. of terms (n)	Sum (S)
1	1	1
1 + 3	2	4
1 + 3 + 5	3	9
1 + 3 + 5 + 7	4	16
1 + 3 + 5 + 7 + 9	a	b
$1 + 3 + 5 + 7 + 9 + \ldots + (2k + 1)$	c	d

Study the number pattern in the table and answer the following questions.
   (a) Write down the numerical values of a and b.
   (b) Find the values of c and d in terms of k.
   (c) Write down a formula connecting S and n.
   (d) Can the sum of the series be 225? Explain your answer.

5.2 Algebra

1. Evaluate
   (a) 5^{-2}, **(b)** $36^{\circ} \times 36^{\frac{1}{2}}$, **(c)** $16^{\frac{3}{4}}$.

2. Given that $a = 2$, $b = -3$ and $c = -7$, evaluate
   (a) $2c^2$, **(b)** $b - a^2$, **(c)** $a(c - b)$.

3. Given that $q = \dfrac{2p + r}{p}$,
   (a) find the value of q when $p = 3$, $r = 6$,
   (b) find the value of p when $q = 10$, $r = 2$.

4. Given that $y + a = \frac{3y + b}{4} - 2$, express

(a) y in terms of a and b, (b) a in terms of y and b,

(c) b in terms of y and a.

5. $x * y$ denotes $\frac{x^2 - y^2}{y}$.

(a) Evaluate $9 * 2$. (b) Evaluate $(10 * 8) * 3$.

(c) Find the value of P such that $P * 5 = 5$.

6. Factorise the following expressions.

(a) $ab - a - b + 1$ (b) $6x^2 + 5x - 6$ (c) $9x^2 - 4$

7. (a) Simplify $\frac{1}{2x^2 + 3x - 2} - \frac{1}{3x^2 + 7x + 2}$.

(b) Given that $B = \frac{Q(1 + 3y)}{2y - m}$, express y in terms of B, Q and m.

(c) Solve the equation $3x + \frac{1}{x} = 6 - x$, giving your answers correct to 2 decimal places.

8. Solve the equation $2x^2 + 5x - 3 = 0$, giving your answers correct to 2 decimal places.

9. (a) Express $\frac{1}{5(x - 3)} + \frac{2}{x + 3}$ as a fraction in the simplest form.

(b) (i) Given that the total cost of $(2x - 5)$ metres of wire at $(x - 4)$ cents per metre is 70 cents, write down an equation in x and show that it reduces to $2x^2 - 13x - 50 = 0$.

(ii) Solve this equation by using formula and give your answers correct to 2 decimal places.

(iii) Use the solution which is a positive number to find the cost of 1 metre of wire.

10. A plane flew from Orchid town, to Sunflower town and then returned to Orchid town. The distance from Orchid town to Sunflower town is approximately 2 400 kilometres.

(a) Travelling from Orchid town, the plane completed the journey in x hours. Write down an expression, in terms of x, for the average speed on the outward journey.

(b) On the return flight, because of a strong headwind, the plane took one hour longer to complete the journey. Write down an expression, in terms of x, for the average speed on the return journey.

(c) The difference in the average speeds of the two flights was 60 kilometres per hour. Form an equation in x and show that it reduces to $x^2 + x - 40 = 0$.

(d) Solve the equation $x^2 + x - 40 = 0$ and hence find the speed on the outward journey.

5.3 Geometry

1. In the diagram, ABC is a straight line and CD is parallel to AE. Given that $AB = BE$, $A\hat{C}E = 30°$, $A\hat{B}E = 50°$, $A\hat{E}B = x°$ and $D\hat{C}E = y°$, calculate
   (a) x,
   (b) y.

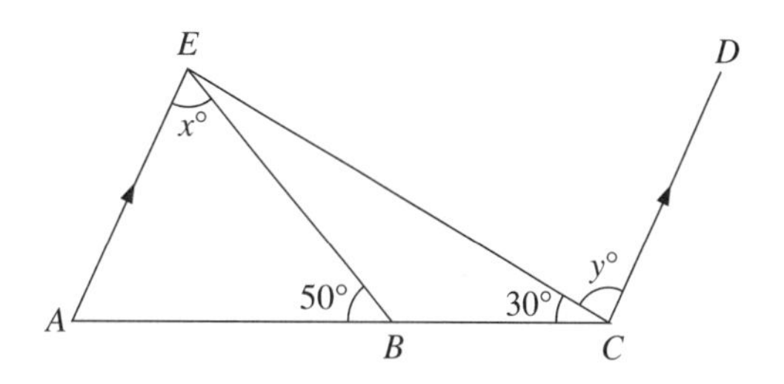

2. Given that O is the centre of the circle, find the values of x and y.

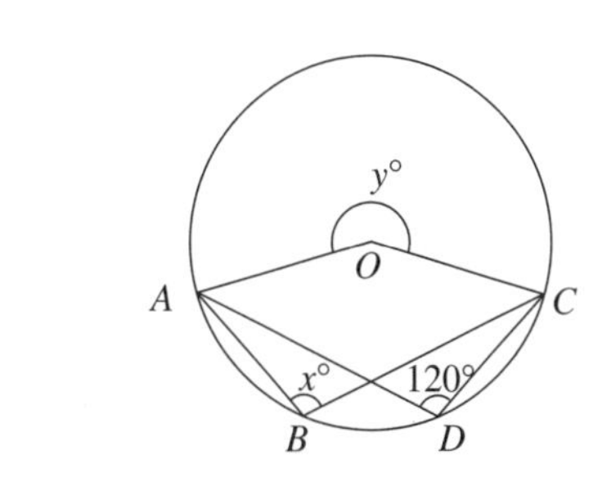

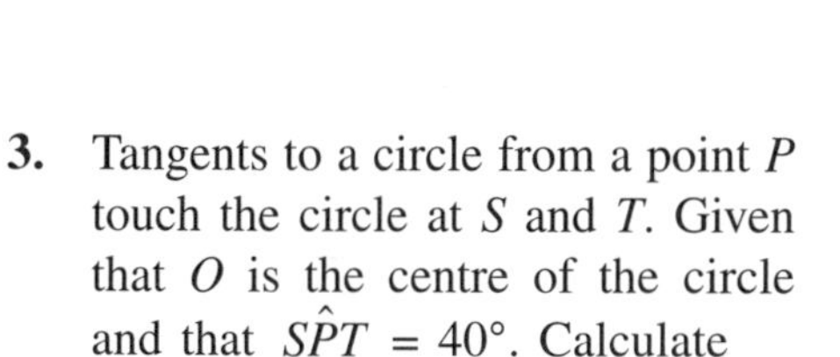

3. Tangents to a circle from a point P touch the circle at S and T. Given that O is the centre of the circle and that $S\hat{P}T = 40°$. Calculate
   (a) $T\hat{O}S$,
   (b) $T\hat{Q}S$.

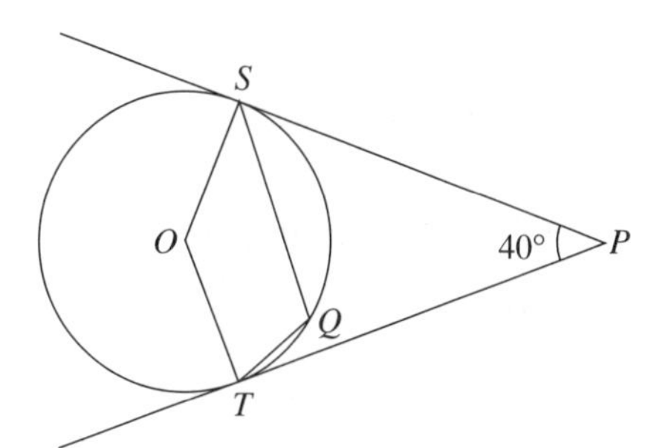

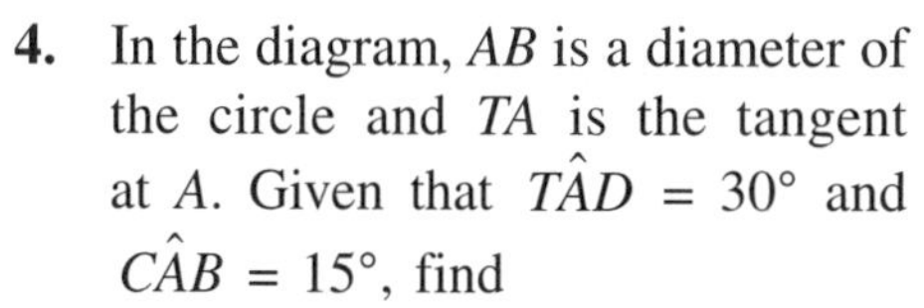

4. In the diagram, AB is a diameter of the circle and TA is the tangent at A. Given that $T\hat{A}D = 30°$ and $C\hat{A}B = 15°$, find
   (a) $A\hat{D}C$,
   (b) $D\hat{B}C$.

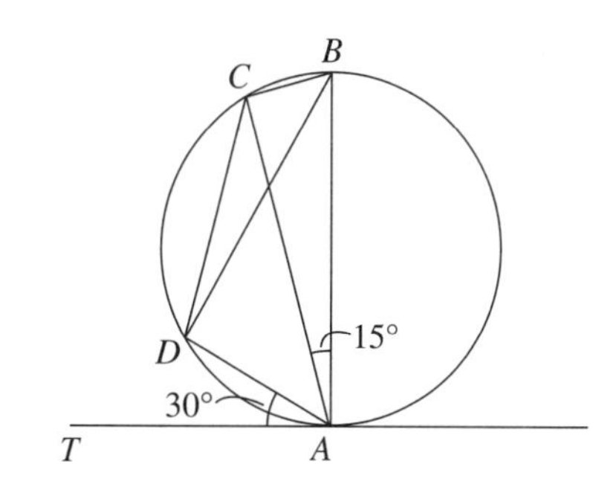

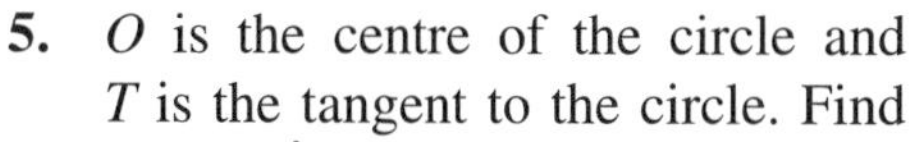

5. O is the centre of the circle and T is the tangent to the circle. Find
   (a) $C\hat{D}O$,
   (b) $A\hat{O}D$,
   (c) $A\hat{D}T$.

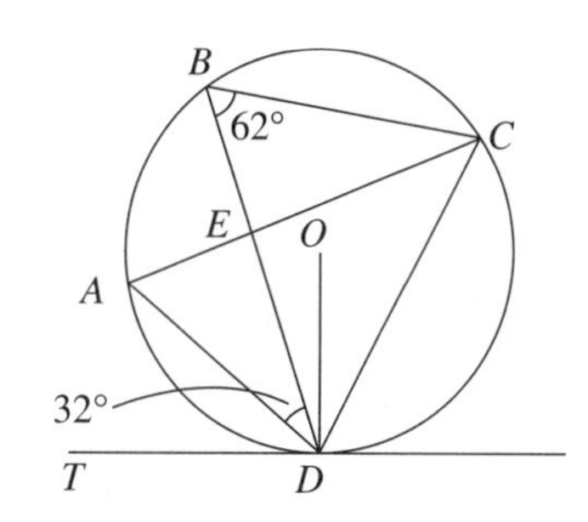

6. **(a)** Calculate the size of an interior angle of a polygon with seven sides.
(b) A second polygon has n sides. Two of its exterior angles are 70° and 80°. The remaining $(n - 2)$ exterior angles are each 14°. Calculate the value of n.

7. **(a)** Each interior angle of a regular polygon is 168°. Find the number of sides of the polygon.
(b) The interior angles of a quadrilateral are in the ratio 2 : 3 : 7 : 8. Find the smallest angle of the quadrilateral.

8.

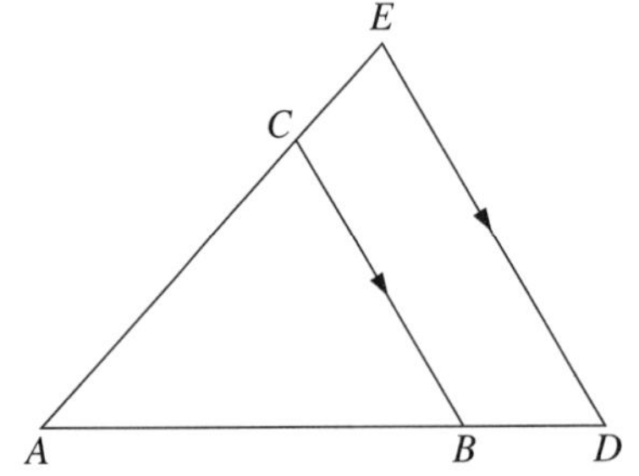

In the figure, $AB = 3BD$ and ED is parallel to CB.
(a) Find the ratio of the area of $\triangle ABC$ to area of $\triangle ADE$.
(b) Given that the area of $\triangle ABC$ is x cm^2, find the area of $BCED$ in terms of x.

9. In the trapezium $ABCD$, AB // DC and $CD = 2BA$. Area of $\triangle CDE = 36$ cm^2. Calculate

(a) the area of $\triangle ABE$,

(b) the ratio of $\frac{BE}{ED}$,

(c) the area of $\triangle BCE$.

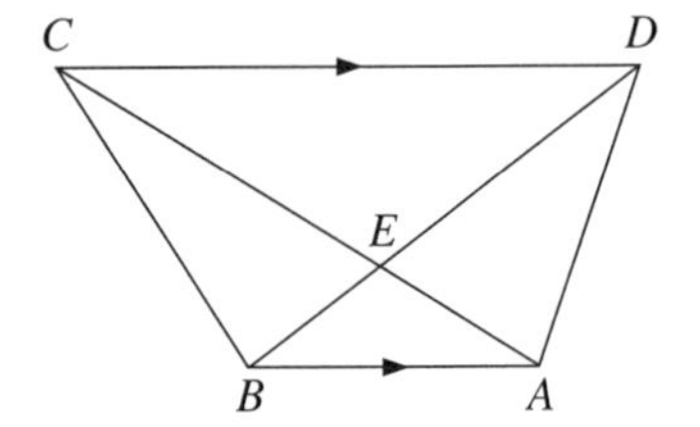

10. **(a)** Write down the number of lines of symmetry of figure I.

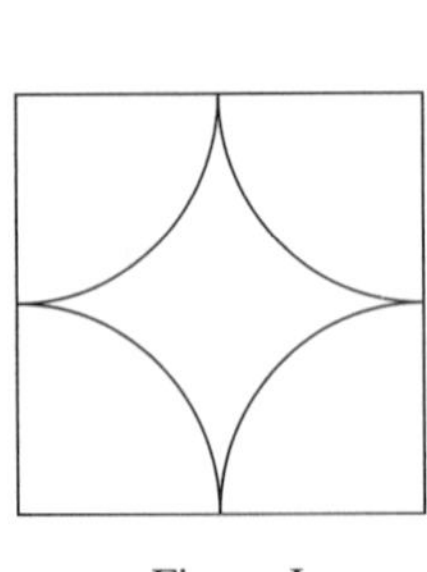

Figure I

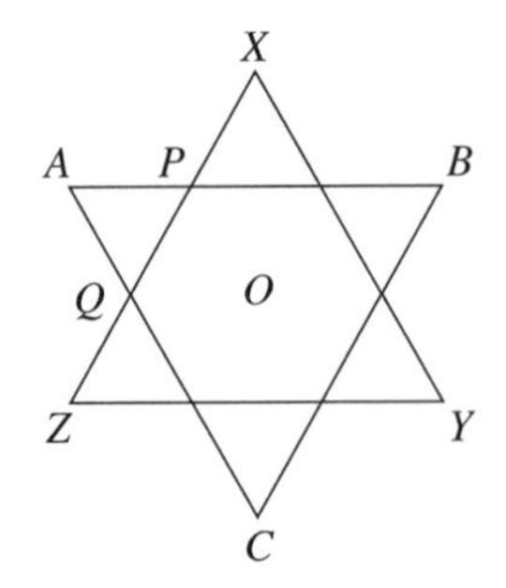

Figure II

(b) **(i)** ABC and XYZ are congruent equilateral triangles. One is placed symmetrically on top of the other as shown in figure II. Draw the axes of symmetry for this figure.
(ii) Given that the area of triangle APQ is 2 cm^2, calculate the area enclosed within the perimeter of the given figure.

5.4 Mensuration

1. The scale of a map is 3 cm : 1.5 km. Express it in the form of 1 : m and find the value of m. Calculate the actual area, in sq. cm, represented by 20 cm^2 on the map.

2. A piece of wire is in the form of an arc of a circle of radius 6 cm subtending 150° at the centre.
   (a) Find the length of the wire in terms of π.
   (b) If the wire is bent into a complete circle, find the radius.

3. The volume of a cone A of radius r cm and height h cm is 120 cm^3. Calculate the volume of another cone
   (a) whose radius is twice that of A, but whose height is $\frac{1}{3}h$,
   (b) which is similar to A, but of height $2h$.
   $\left[\text{Volume of cone} = \frac{1}{3} \times \text{base area} \times \text{height}\right]$

4. 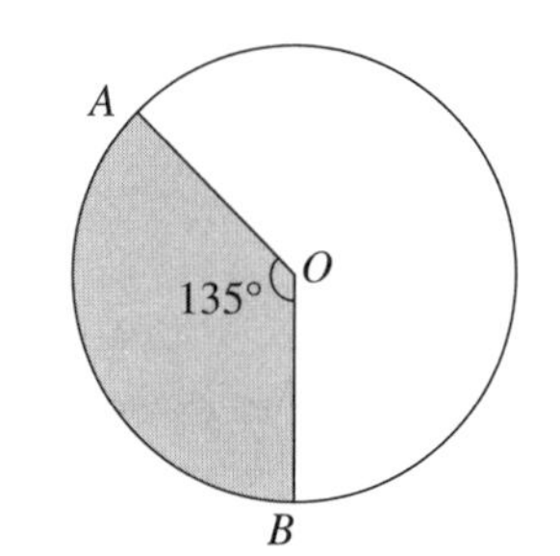

   In the diagram, O is the centre of the circle of radius 14 cm, and $A\hat{O}B$ = 135°. Taking $\pi = \frac{22}{7}$, calculate
   (a) the circumference of the circle,
   (b) the length of the major arc AB,
   (c) the area of the shaded sector AOB.

5. 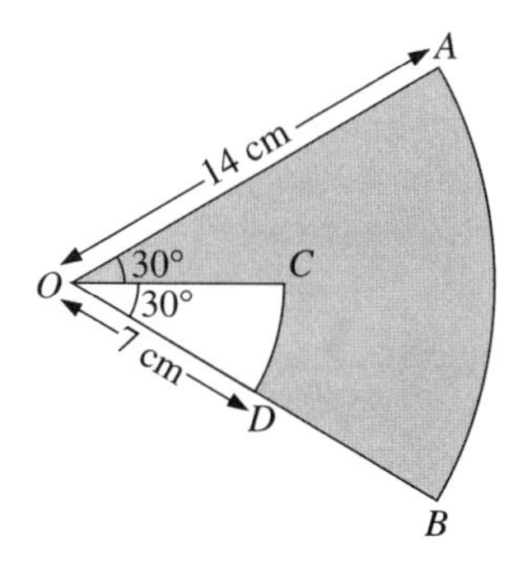

   The diagram comprises two sectors with angles 30° and 60°, their radii are 7 cm and 14 cm respectively. Both have centre O. Find in terms of fraction,
   (a) the area of the shaded region,
   (b) the perimeter of the shaded region.

6. 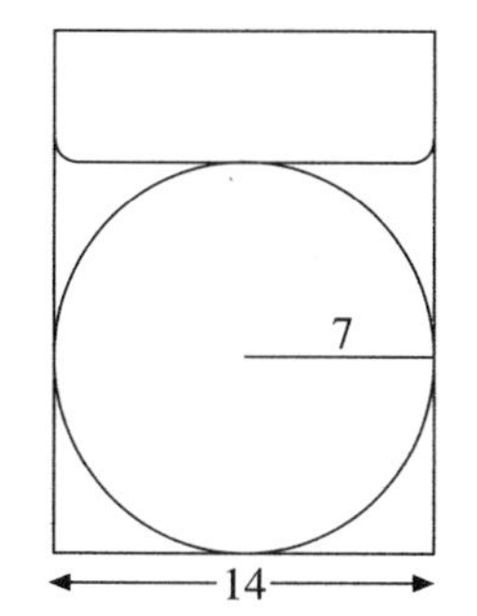

   A sphere is placed into a cylindrical can containing water so that the water just covers the sphere. The diagram shows the cross-section of the sphere in the can. The diameter of the can is 14 cm. Calculate
   (a) the total surface area of the can which is in contact with the water when the sphere is in the can,
   (b) the volume of water in the can.
   $\left[\text{Take } \pi = \frac{22}{7}; \text{ volume of sphere} = \frac{4}{3}\pi r^3\right]$

7. This diagram shows a new logo, designed in red, white and green, for a car company. The radius of the circle is 5 cm. The three red sectors each have an angle of 30° at the centre of the circle. The three white triangles each have a right angle at the centre of the circle. Taking the value of π to be 3.142, calculate

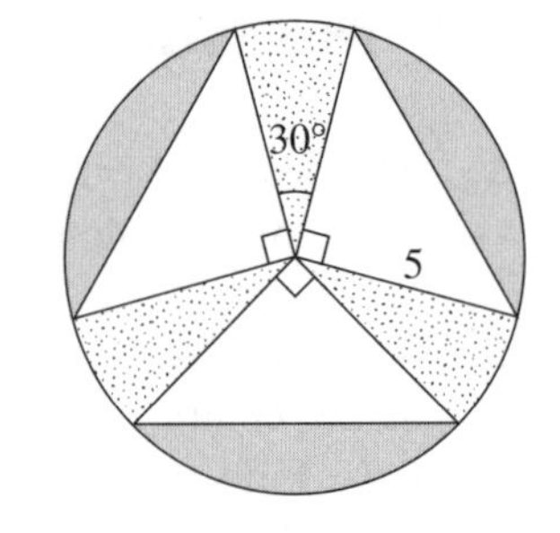

(a) the length of an arc of a red sector,
(b) the area of a red sector,
(c) the area of a green segment.

8.

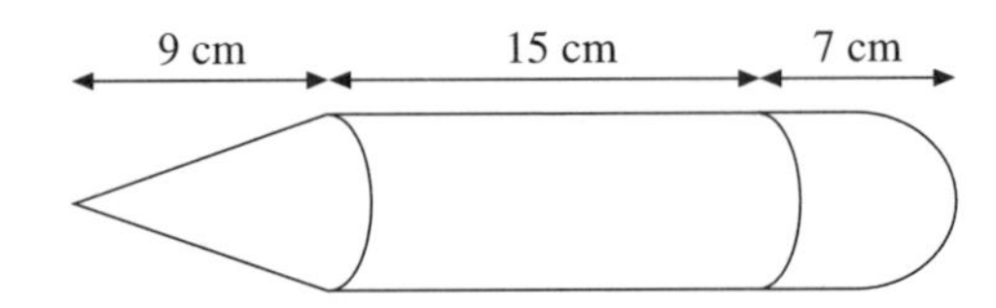

A model consists of a solid cone and a solid hemisphere attached to a solid cylinder as shown in the diagram.

(a) Calculate the volume of the model.
(b) Given that the model is made from a material of density 0.4 g/cm^3, calculate its mass.
(c) Calculate the total surface area of the model.

9.

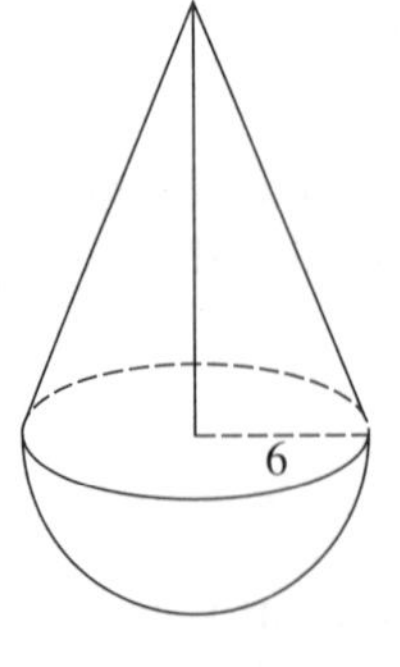

Figure I

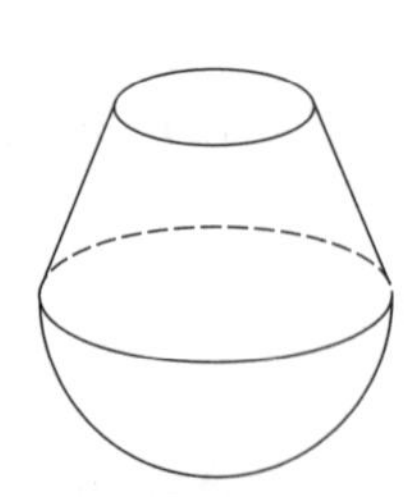

Figure II

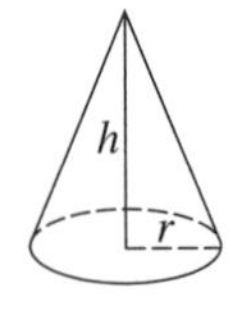

Figure III

Figure I shows a solid consisting of a right circular cone and a hemisphere with a common base which is a circle of radius 6 m.

(a) Find the volume of the hemisphere (leave your answer in terms of π).
(b) It is given that the volume of the cone is equal to $\frac{4}{3}$ of the volume of the hemisphere. Show that the height of the cone is 16 m.

The solid is then cut into two parts, figures II and III. The upper part is a right circular cone of height h and radius r.

(c) Express r in terms of h.
(d) Given further that the ratio of the volume of figure III to figure II is 1 : 6, find
   (i) the value of h,
   (ii) the volume of a cone similar to figure III with a surface area that is four times that of the cone in figure III (leave your answer in terms of π).

$\left[\text{Volume of a sphere} = \frac{4}{3}\pi r^3\text{; volume of a cone} = \frac{1}{3}\pi r^2 h\right]$

10. A model consists of a solid cuboid attached to a solid pyramid as shown in the diagram. The height of the cuboid is 24 cm and the area of the base is 96 cm^2.

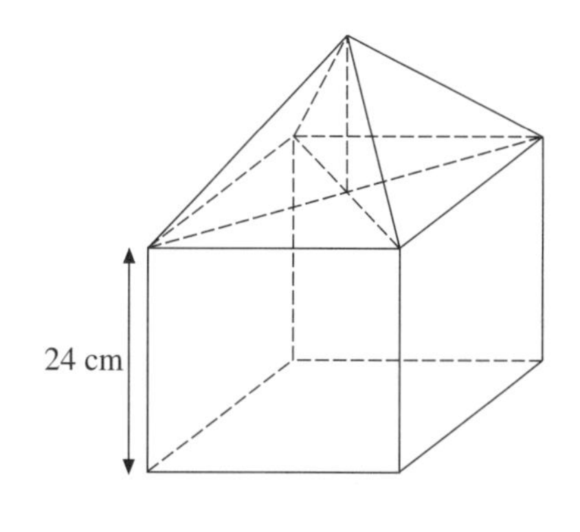

(a) Calculate the volume of the cuboid.
(b) Given that the volume of the pyramid is 144 cm^3, calculate the height of the pyramid.
(c) Given that the model is made from a material of density 0.5 g/cm^3, calculate its mass in kg.
(d) Given that the width and length of the base of the cuboid are in the ratio of 2 : 3, calculate the width and length of the cuboid.

$\left[\text{Volume of a pyramid} = \frac{1}{3} \times \text{base area} \times \text{height}\right]$

5.5 Trigonometry and Bearings

1. In the triangle, the point B lies on AC such that AB = 16 cm, BC = 12 cm, CD = 5 cm and $A\hat{C}D$ = 90°. Find the value of

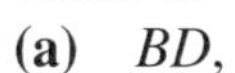

(a) BD,
(b) $\sin B\hat{D}C$,
(c) $\cos A\hat{B}D$.

2. Points A, B and C are on level ground. A is the foot of a vertical flagpole AT of height 20 m. AB = 30 m, AC = 47 m and $B\hat{A}C$ = 125°.

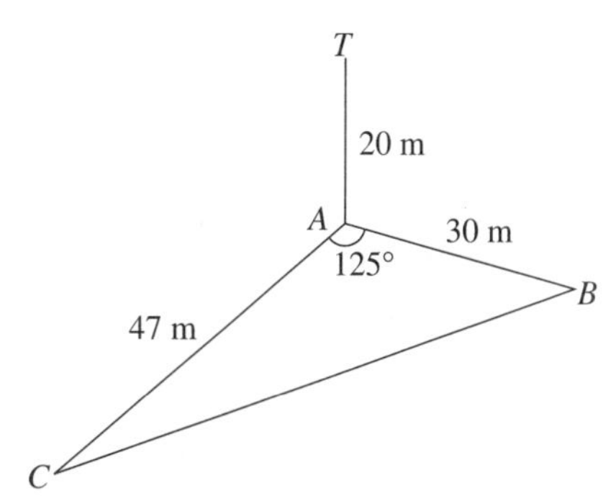

(a) Calculate
   (i) BC,
   (ii) the angle of elevation of the top of the flagpole from C,
   (iii) the area of triangle ABC.
(b) A man walks from B to C. Find the maximum angle of elevation of the top of the flagpole from the man during the walk.

3. The bearing of B from A is 052°, the bearing of C from A is 108° and $AB = AC$. Calculate
   (a) the bearing of A from B,
   (b) $A\hat{B}C$,
   (c) the bearing of C from B.

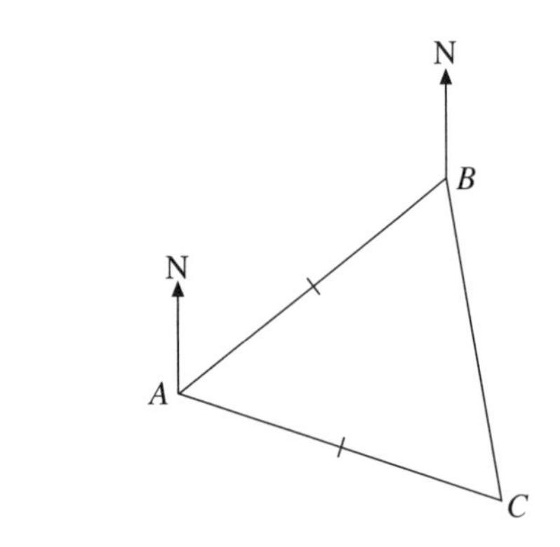

4. In the diagram, $BN = 5$ cm, $DN = 2$ cm, $CD = 7$ cm, $B\hat{A}N = 40°$ and $A\hat{N}B = 90°$. BNC is a straight line. Calculate
   (a) CN,
   (b) AB,
   (c) AD,
   (d) $A\hat{C}B$.

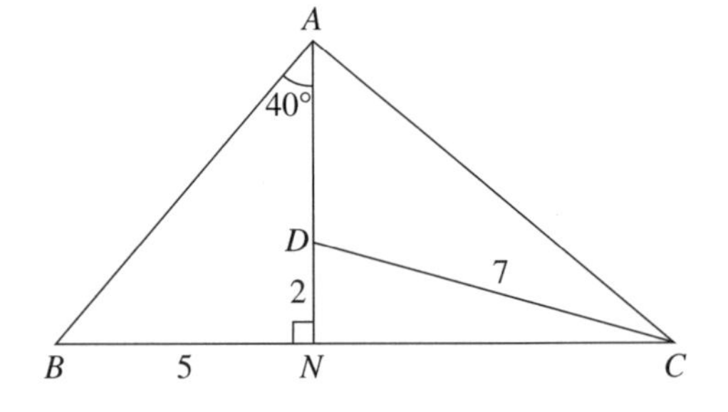

5. A and B are two points along a straight road running west to east and they are 200 metres apart. The bearings of a building D from A and B are 034° and 298° respectively.
   (a) Find the distance of the building from the road.
   (b) If a place C on the road is 120 metres from the building, what is the bearing of C from the building?

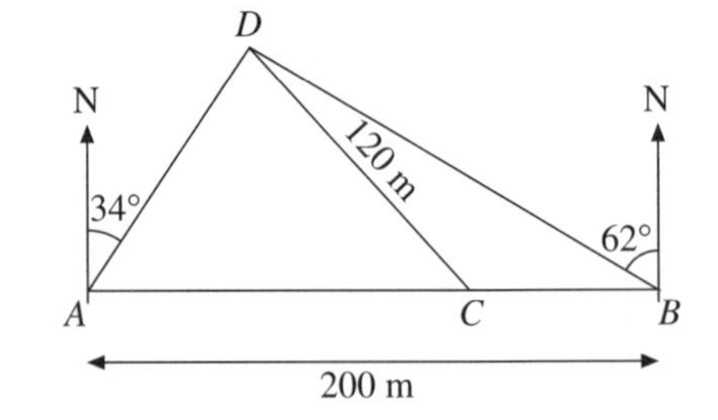

6. The diagram shows a pyramid whose base is a rectangle with sides 12 cm and 5 cm. The vertex T of the pyramid is 12 cm vertically above D. Calculate
   (a) BD,
   (b) the angle of elevation of T from C,
   (c) write down the value of tan $T\hat{A}D$, giving your answer as a fraction.

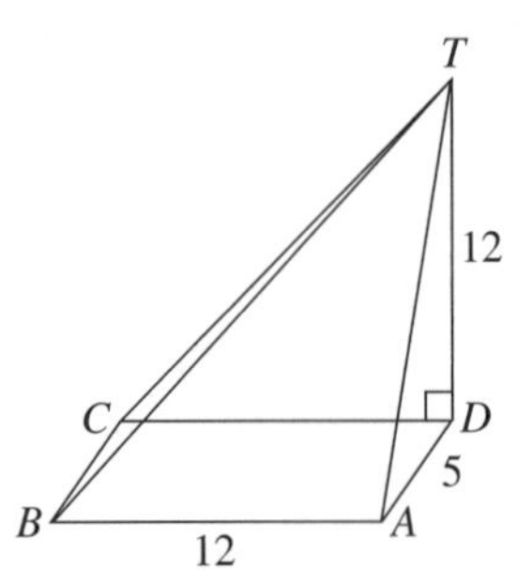

7. In the diagram, AB represents a tall building and CD represents a shorter building of height 10 m. It is given that X is due south of A, C is due east of A, $XA = 40$ m, $XC = 75$ m and the angle of elevation of B, the top of the building, from X is 39.5°. Calculate

(a) the height of the building AB,
(b) the length of AC,
(c) the angle of elevation of B from D,
(d) the angle AXC.

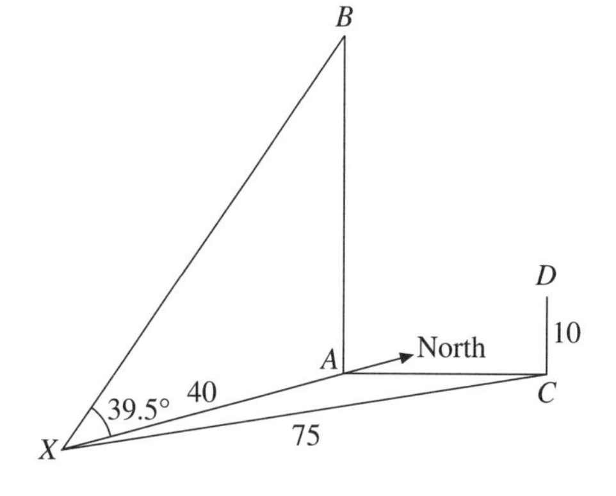

8. **(a)** A, B and C are three observation posts in the same horizontal plane. B is 800 m due east of A, and C is such that $AC = 300$ m and $BC = 700$ m as shown in the diagram. Calculate the bearing of C from A.

(b) P is the foot of a vertical radio mast on the line AB, 100 m from A. X is the top of the mast. The angle of elevation of the top of the mast from A is 12°. Calculate the height of the mast.

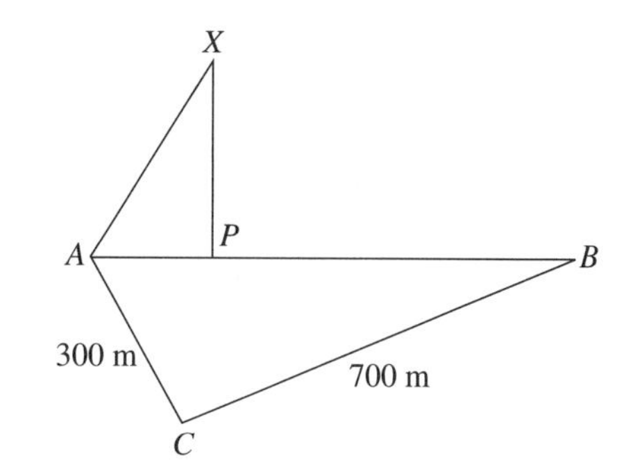

(c) Q is a point on the AC line and lies due south of P. Calculate
(i) the angle of elevation of the top of the mast from Q,
(ii) the distance BQ.

9. In the diagram, A, B and C represent three islands. B is 25 km from A on a bearing of 040°. C is 36 km from A on a bearing of 125°. Calculate

(a) the bearing of A from C,
(b) the distance of C from B,
(c) the area of triangle ABC.

A ship sails from A directly to C at a steady speed of 20 km/h. The ship is closest to B at the point X.

(d) Calculate the distance XB.
(e) Find the time taken, in minutes, to the nearest minute, for the ship to reach X.

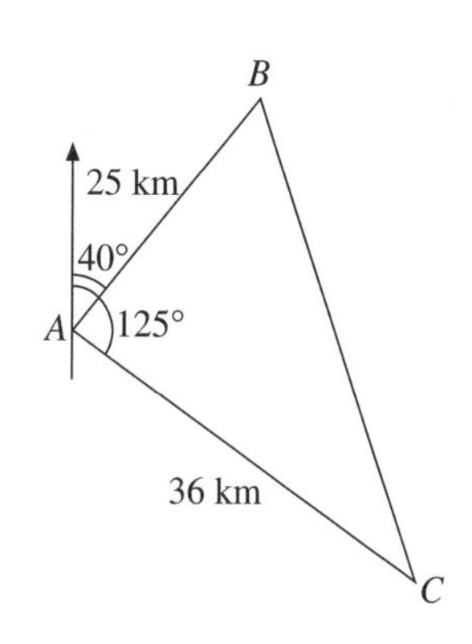

10. $ABCDEF$ is a wedge and $ABCD$ is a rectangular plane inclined at an angle of 30° to the rectangular plane $ABFE$. CF and DE are perpendicular to plane $ABFE$. Given also that $C\hat{A}B = 53°$ and $CF = h$ mm. Using as much of the information given below as is necessary, calculate

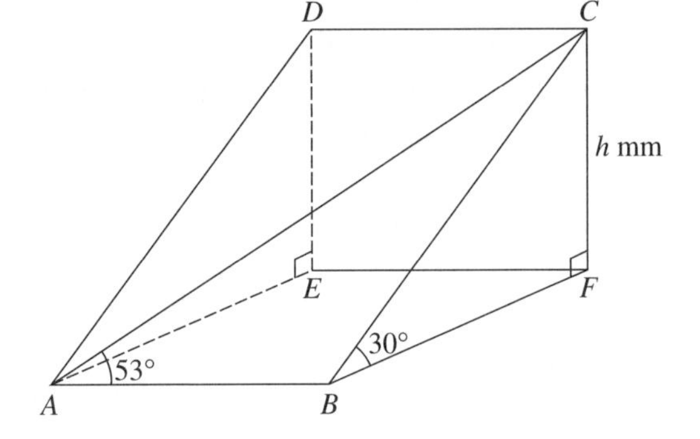

(a) the lengths of BC and AC in terms of h,
(b) the value of $\sin C\hat{A}F$,
(c) the value of AB if $h = 12$.
[sin 53° = 0.80, cos 53° = 0.60, tan 53° = 1.33,
sin 30° = 0.50, cos 30° = 0.87, tan 30° = 0.58]

5.6 Loci

1. Answer this question on a sheet of plain paper.
(a) Construct triangle ABC in which $BC = 10$ cm, angle $ABC = 30°$ and angle $ACB = 90°$. Measure and write the length of AB.
(b) On the same diagram, construct
(i) on the same side of BC as A, the locus of a point P such that the area of triangle $PBC = \frac{1}{2}$ area of triangle ABC,
(ii) the locus of points equidistant from B and C,
(iii) the locus of a point Q such that angle $BQC = 90°$,
(iv) a point X such that angle $BXC = 90°$ and area of triangle $BXC = \frac{1}{2}$ area of triangle BAC.

2. **(a)** In the diagram below, draw the locus of points which are equidistant from the two parallel lines AB and CD.
(b) Describe the locus of point P such that $A\hat{P}B = 90°$, given that AB is 10 cm.

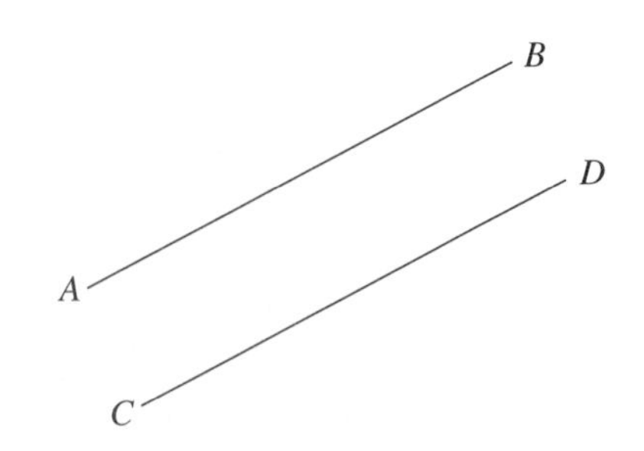

3. Answer this question on a sheet of plain paper.
Construct the triangle ABC in which $AB = 10$ cm and $C\hat{A}B = C\hat{B}A = 50°$. Measure and write down the length of AC. On the same diagram, and on the same side of AB as C, construct and label clearly,
(a) the locus of points P such that the area of triangle $APB = 20$ cm^2,
(b) the locus of points Q such that $A\hat{Q}B = 40°$.

4. (a) Construct triangle PQR in which $PQ = 5$ cm, $QR = 6$ cm and $PR = 8.5$ cm. Draw also, on the same diagram, an isosceles triangle PSR, in which $PS = SR = 7$ cm and S lies on the opposite side of PR to Q. Measure and write down the size of $Q\hat{R}S$.
   (b) On the same diagram, construct
      (i) the locus of points equidistant from R and Q,
      (ii) the locus of points equidistant from RQ and PQ.
   (c) A point X lies inside the quadrilateral $PQRS$. The position of X is such that $P\hat{Q}X = R\hat{Q}X$ and $RX = QX$. Measure and write down the length of SX.

5. Answer this question on a sheet of plain paper.
   (a) Construct triangle ABC in which $AB = 10.8$ cm, $BC = 8.2$ cm and $A\hat{B}C = 110°$.

   On the same diagram, draw
   (b) the locus of points that are equidistant from AB and BC,
   (c) the locus of points that are 3.5 cm from the line BC and on the same side of BC as A,
   (d) a circle of radius 3.5 cm which has AB and BC as tangents and label the centre of the circle with the letter O.

6. A field is in the form of a quadrilateral $ABCD$ with $AB = 70$ m, $B\hat{A}D = 110°$, $A\hat{B}C = 100°$, diagonal $BD = 110$ m and $A\hat{D}C = 60°$.
   (a) Using a scale of 1 cm to represent 10 m, construct an accurate scale drawing of the field.

   In a contest, a prize is hidden at a point on the field. It is 45 m from point A and equidistant from CD and CB. On your drawing, construct the locus which represents
   (b) (i) all points on the field which are 45 m from point A,
      (ii) all points on the field which are equidistant from the lines CD and CB.
   (c) Label, with the letter P, the point representing the position where the prize is hidden.
   (d) A portion of the field is to be cornered off. The region affected is to be within 45 m from A and nearer to point D than point C. Indicate by shading the affected region.

7. Answer this question on a sheet of plain paper.
   (a) Construct the triangle ABC in which $AB = 12$ cm, $BC = 9$ cm and $AC = 8$ cm.
   (b) On your diagram, construct
      (i) the locus of X which moves so that it is equidistant from AB and BC,
      (ii) the locus of points Y which moves so that $A\hat{Y}C = 90°$,
      (iii) the locus of points Z which moves so that the area of triangle AZB is 24 cm^2.
   (c) The point P, inside the triangle ABC is such that $P\hat{B}C \leqslant P\hat{B}A$, $A\hat{P}C \geqslant 90°$ and area of $A\hat{P}B \leqslant 24 \text{ cm}^2$. Indicate clearly, by shading, the region in which the point P must lie.

8. Answer this question on a sheet of plain paper.
Tony, Peter and John are standing in a field such that Peter is 9 m due east of Tony and John is at a bearing of 020° from Tony who is 7 m away. In a single diagram,
(a) construct the positions of the three boys, using 1 cm to represent 1 m,
(b) measure, and write down the actual distance Peter is away from John,
(c) draw the locus of points which are 5 m from John,
(d) draw the locus of points which are equidistant from the line joining Tony and Peter and the line joining John and Peter,
(e) indicate clearly the region in which a fourth boy can move such that he is nearer to Tony and Peter than to Peter and John, and must be 5 m from John.

9. Answer this question on a sheet of plain paper.
(a) Using ruler and compasses only, construct $\triangle ABC$ such that $BC = 7$ cm, $AB = 4$ cm and $AC = 5$ cm.
(b) On the same diagram, draw
(i) the locus of points which are equidistant from B and C,
(ii) the locus of points which are equidistant from CB and CA,
(iii) the locus of a point P which moves inside $\triangle ABC$ such that the area of $\triangle ABC$ = 2(area of $\triangle ABP$).
(c) A point Q lies inside $\triangle ABC$ such that $Q\hat{C}B = Q\hat{C}A$ and the area of $\triangle ABC$ = 2(area of $\triangle ABQ$). Mark and label the point Q.

10. Answer this question on a sheet of plain paper.
(a) Construct full size, triangle LMN in which $LM = 11.6$ cm, $L\hat{M}N = 65°$ and $MN = 7.5$ cm. Measure and write down the size of $L\hat{N}M$.
(b) On your diagram, draw the loci of points within the triangle which are
(i) 8 cm from L,
(ii) equidistant from L and M,
(iii) equidistant from LM and LN.
(c) A point Z inside the triangle is such that it is
(i) less than 8 cm from L,
(ii) nearer to M than to L,
(iii) nearer to LN than to LM.
On your diagram, indicate by shading the region in which Z must lie.

5.7 Vectors

1. It is given that P is the point $(-3, 2)$, Q is the point $(12, -10)$ and A is the point on PQ such that $PA = \frac{1}{2}AQ$. Express as column vectors
(a) $\overrightarrow{PQ}$, **(b)** $\overrightarrow{PA}$,
(c) the position vector of A relative to the origin O.

2. **(a)** Given that O is the origin. A, B and C are the points (8, 4), (5, 5) and (–1, –3) respectively. Find

(i) the coordinates of P if $\overrightarrow{OP} = \frac{1}{2}\overrightarrow{OA} + \overrightarrow{OC}$,

(ii) $|\overrightarrow{BC}|$.

(b)

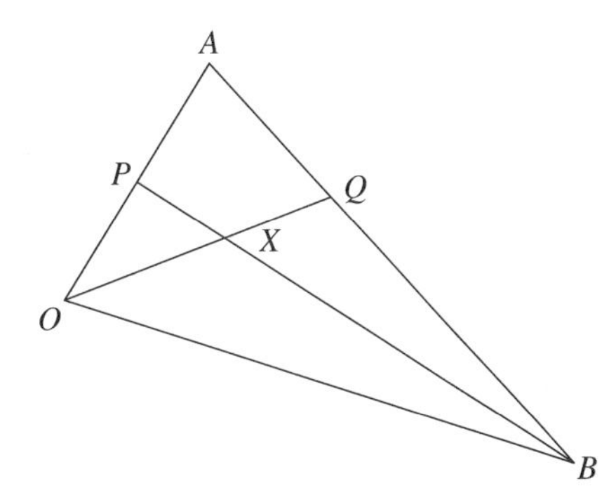

In triangle OAB, P is the midpoint of OA, Q is a point on AB such that $AQ = \frac{1}{3}AB$ and BP and OQ meet at X. If $\overrightarrow{OA} = \mathbf{a}$ and $\overrightarrow{OB} = \mathbf{b}$, express the vectors $\overrightarrow{OQ}$ and $\overrightarrow{BP}$ in terms of **a** and **b**. Let $\overrightarrow{BX} = m\overrightarrow{BP}$ and $\overrightarrow{OX} = n\overrightarrow{OQ}$, express the vector $\overrightarrow{BX}$ in two different ways in terms of **a**, **b**, m and n. Hence deduce

(i) the values of m and n,

(ii) the ratio, $\dfrac{\text{area of } \triangle POX}{\text{area of } \triangle BOX}$.

3. If $\overrightarrow{OP} = \begin{pmatrix} 5 \\ 3 \end{pmatrix}$, $\overrightarrow{PQ} = \begin{pmatrix} -2 \\ 1 \end{pmatrix}$ and $R = \begin{pmatrix} -1 \\ h \end{pmatrix}$. Find

(a) the column vector of Q,

(b) $|\overrightarrow{PQ}|$,

(c) the coordinates of R if $\overrightarrow{PR}$ is parallel to $\overrightarrow{PQ}$.

4. It is given that $\mathbf{p} = \begin{pmatrix} 3 \\ 2 \end{pmatrix}$, $\mathbf{q} = \begin{pmatrix} -2 \\ 4 \end{pmatrix}$ and $\mathbf{r} = \begin{pmatrix} a \\ b \end{pmatrix}$.

(a) Find $|\mathbf{q}|$.

(b) Express $3\mathbf{p} - \frac{1}{2}\mathbf{q}$ as a column vector.

(c) Given that $\mathbf{p} - \mathbf{q} = 2\mathbf{r}$, find the value of a and of b.

5.

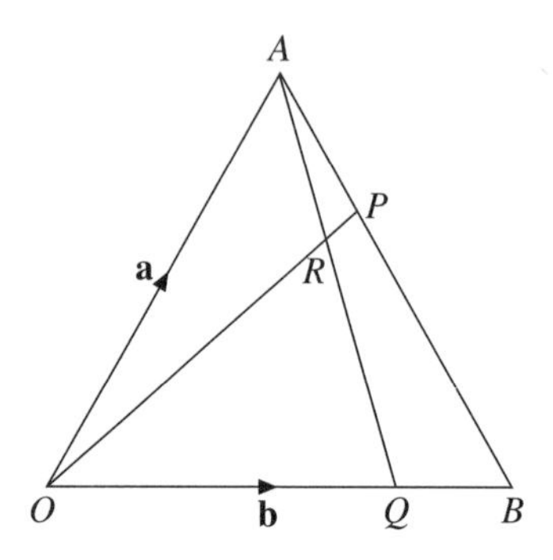

In the diagram, $\overrightarrow{OA} = \mathbf{a}$ and $\overrightarrow{OB} = \mathbf{b}$. The points P and Q lie on AB and OB respectively so that $\frac{AP}{PB} = \frac{1}{3}$ and $\frac{OQ}{OB} = \frac{3}{4}$.

(a) Express $\overrightarrow{AQ}$ in terms of $\mathbf{a}$ and $\mathbf{b}$ and show that $\overrightarrow{OP} = \frac{1}{4}(3\mathbf{a} + \mathbf{b})$.

(b) The lines OP and AQ intersect at point R. Given that $\overrightarrow{AR} = k\overrightarrow{AQ}$, show that $\overrightarrow{OR} = (1 - k)\mathbf{a} + \frac{3}{7}k\mathbf{b}$.

(c) By taking $\overrightarrow{OR} = h\overrightarrow{OP}$, and using the results in **(a)** and **(b)**, form an equation connecting $\mathbf{a}$, $\mathbf{b}$, h and k. Use this equation to find the values of h and k.

(d) Write down the numerical values of the ratios $AR : RQ$ and $OR : OP$.

6.

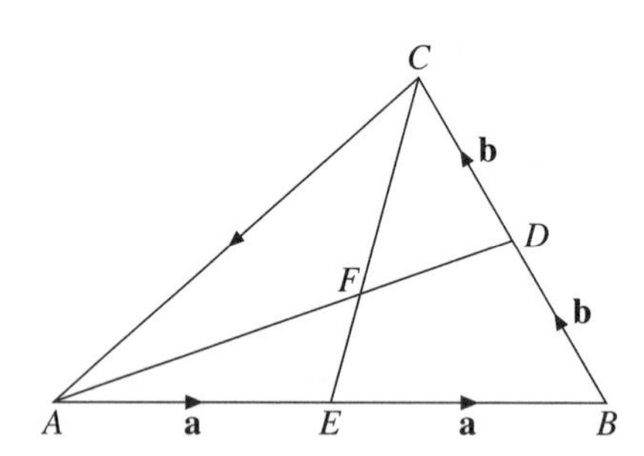

In triangle ABC, D and E are midpoints of BC and AB respectively.

(a) Given that $\overrightarrow{AB} = 2\mathbf{a}$ and $\overrightarrow{BC} = 2\mathbf{b}$, express $\overrightarrow{CA}$ in terms of $\mathbf{a}$ and $\mathbf{b}$.

(b) Given that $\overrightarrow{AF} = h\overrightarrow{AD}$ and $\overrightarrow{CF} = k\overrightarrow{CE}$, express as simply as possible, $\overrightarrow{AF}$ and $\overrightarrow{CF}$ in terms of $\mathbf{a}$, $\mathbf{b}$, h and k.

(c) Hence form an equation involving $\mathbf{a}$, $\mathbf{b}$, h and k and use it to find the values of h and k.

(d) Find the numerical value of $\frac{\text{area of } \triangle ABC}{\text{area of } \triangle AEF}$.

(e) If M is the midpoint of AC, show that the points B, F and M are collinear.

7.

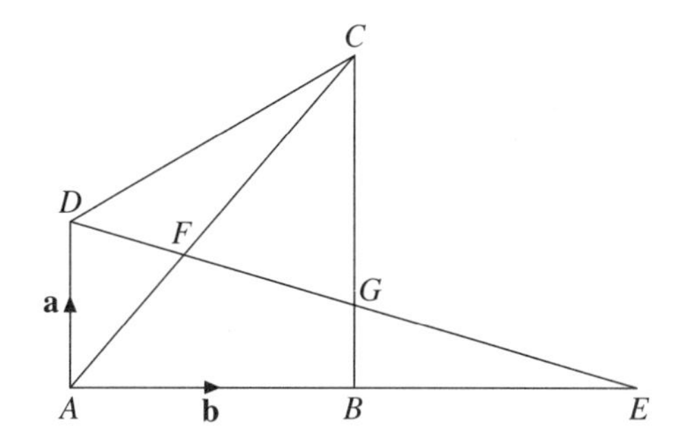

In the diagram, $ABCD$ is a trapezium with AD parallel to BC and $BC = 2AD$. AB is produced to E so that $AE = 2AB$. DE cuts AC and BC at F and G respectively.

(a) Given that $\overrightarrow{AD} = \mathbf{a}$ and $\overrightarrow{AB} = \mathbf{b}$, express as simply as possible in terms of $\mathbf{a}$ and/or $\mathbf{b}$,

(i) $\overrightarrow{BC}$,

(ii) $\overrightarrow{DC}$,

(iii) $\overrightarrow{DE}$.

(b) Given that $\dfrac{DF}{DE} = h$, express $\overrightarrow{DF}$ in terms of h, $\mathbf{a}$ and $\mathbf{b}$.

(c) Given that $\dfrac{CF}{CA} = k$, express $\overrightarrow{CF}$ in terms of k, $\mathbf{a}$ and $\mathbf{b}$.

(d) Using the expressions for $\overrightarrow{DF}$, $\overrightarrow{CF}$ and $\overrightarrow{DC}$, form an equation connecting h, k, $\mathbf{a}$ and $\mathbf{b}$. Use this equation to find the values of h and k.

(e) Deduce the numerical value of the ratio $\dfrac{\text{area of } \triangle ADF}{\text{area of } \triangle AFE}$.

8. In the following diagram, $OABC$ is a parallelogram with $\overrightarrow{OA} = 3\mathbf{a}$ and $\overrightarrow{OC} = \mathbf{b}$. P is a point on OA such that $OP : OA = 1 : 3$. Q is the point of intersection between AC and PB.

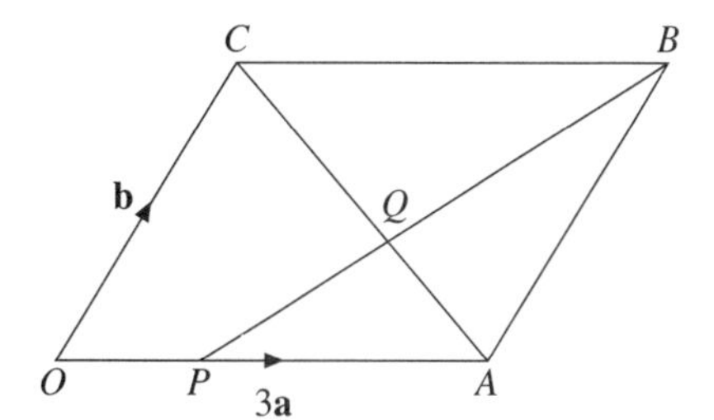

(a) Express the vectors in terms of $\mathbf{a}$ and $\mathbf{b}$,

(i) $\overrightarrow{OP}$,

(ii) $\overrightarrow{AC}$,

(iii) $\overrightarrow{PB}$.

(b) Given that $\overrightarrow{AQ} = k\overrightarrow{AC}$, show that $\overrightarrow{PQ} = (2 - 3k)\mathbf{a} + k\mathbf{b}$.

(c) Given also that $\overrightarrow{AQ} = h\overrightarrow{PB}$, calculate the value of k and of h.

9. In triangle OBC, A is the midpoint of OB.

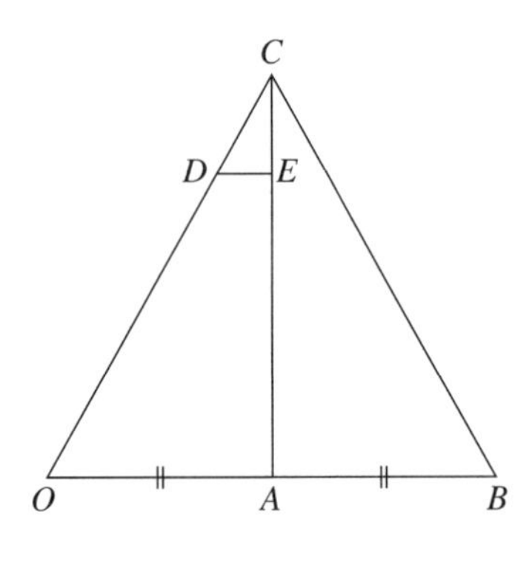

(a) Given that $\overrightarrow{OB} = \mathbf{b}$, and $\overrightarrow{OC} = \mathbf{c}$, express in terms of $\mathbf{b}$ and/or $\mathbf{c}$, the vectors

(i) $\overrightarrow{OA}$,

(ii) $\overrightarrow{CA}$.

(b) Given that E is the point on AC such that $\overrightarrow{AE} = \frac{3}{4}\overrightarrow{AC}$ and that $\overrightarrow{DC} = h\overrightarrow{OC}$, express $\overrightarrow{DE}$ in terms of h, $\mathbf{b}$ and $\mathbf{c}$.

(c) Given that DE is parallel to OA, find the numerical value of

(i) h,

(ii) $\dfrac{DE}{OB}$,

(iii) $\dfrac{\text{area of } \triangle DEC}{\text{area of } \triangle OBC}$.

10. In the diagram, $\overrightarrow{OS} = \mathbf{a}$ and $\overrightarrow{OQ} = \mathbf{b}$.

$OS = \frac{1}{2}OP$, $OR = 2OQ$ and $PT = \frac{2}{3}PQ$.

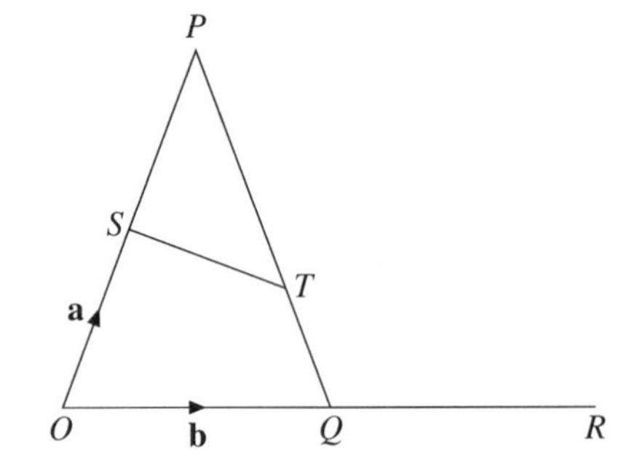

(a) Express as simply as possible in terms of $\mathbf{a}$ and/or $\mathbf{b}$, the vectors

(i) $\overrightarrow{PQ}$,

(ii) $\overrightarrow{TQ}$,

(iii) $\overrightarrow{ST}$.

(b) Prove that ST, when produced, will pass through R.

(c) It is given that $\mathbf{a} = \begin{pmatrix} 2 \\ 5 \end{pmatrix}$, calculate $|\mathbf{a}|$.

5.8 Graphs

1. (a) A straight line passes through the points $X(1, -1)$, $Y(4, 1)$ and $Z(k, 3)$. Find the value of k.

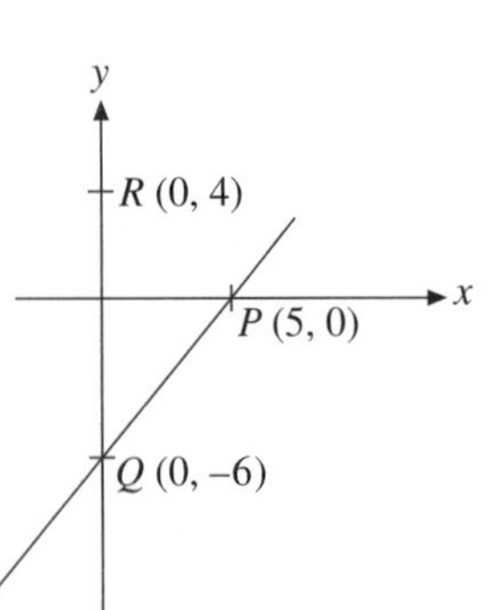

(b) In the diagram, P is the point $(5, 0)$, Q is the point $(0, -6)$ and R is the point $(0, 4)$.

(i) Find the equation of the line PQ.

(ii) Calculate the area of $\triangle PQR$.

(iii) Calculate the coordinates of a fourth vertex, S, such that $PQSR$ forms a parallelogram.

2.

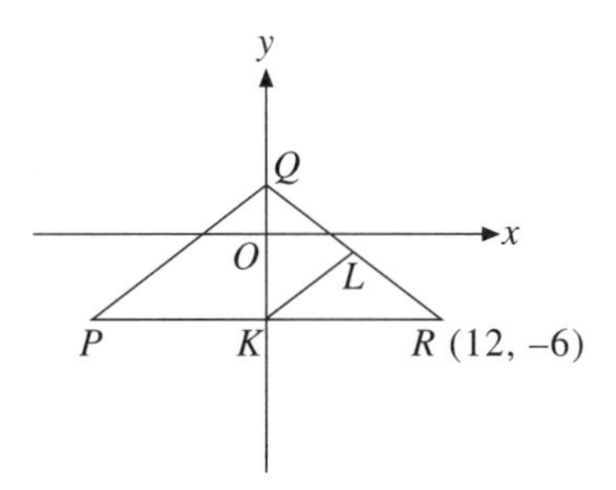

In the diagram, R is the point (12, –6) and PR is parallel to the x-axis. Given that K and L are the midpoints of PR and QR respectively, and that $OK = 2OQ$, find

(a) the gradient of QR,

(b) the equation of line KL,

(c) the area of $\triangle KQL$.

3. The curve $y = a + bx - x^2$ passes through the points $P(1, 12)$ and $Q(2, 12)$.

(a) Show that $a + b = 13$ and write down another equation involving a and b. Find the value of a and of b.

(b) Find the coordinates of the point at which the curve crosses the y-axis.

4.

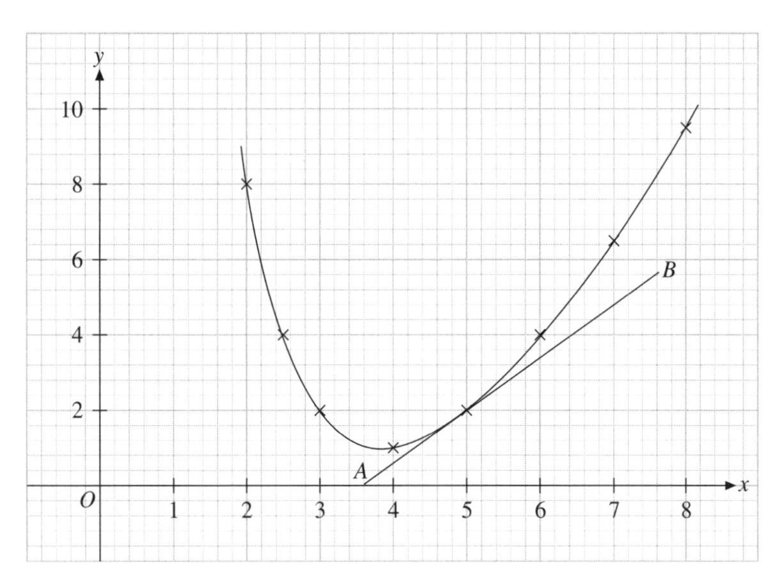

The diagram shows the graph of $y = 4x + \frac{60}{x} - 30$.

(a) AB is the tangent to the curve at the point where $x = 5$ and hence, estimate the gradient of the curve at this point.

(b) By drawing a suitable line on the diagram, find from the graph, a solution of the equation $4x + \frac{60}{x} - 33 = 0$.

(c) Find the range of values of x for which y is less than 8.

5. Answer this question on a sheet of graph paper.
The variables x and y are connected by the equation $y = x^3 - 3x - 2$ and some corresponding values are given in the following table.

x	–3	–2	–1	0	1	2	3
y	–20	a	0	–2	– 4	0	b

Calculate the values of a and b.
Taking 2 cm to represent 1 unit on the x-axis and 2 cm to represent 4 units on the y-axis, draw the graph of $y = x^3 - 3x - 2$ for $-3 \leqslant x \leqslant 3$.

(a) From your graph, find
   (i) the least value of y,
   (ii) the values of x when $y = -2$.

(b) Find, by drawing a tangent, the gradient of the graph at the point when $x = 2$.

(c) By drawing a suitable straight line on the axis, use your graph to find the solutions of the equation
$$x^3 - 3x - 2 = 5x + 4.$$

(d) Using your graph or otherwise, estimate the area enclosed by
$$x = 0,\ x = 3 \text{ and } y = 0.$$

6. Answer this question on a sheet of graph paper.
The values of x and y are connected by the equation:
$$y = \frac{3(x - 1)(x + 2)}{x - 4}$$

x	–5	– 4	–3	–2	–1	0	1	2
y	–6	–3.75	a	0	1.2	b	0	–6

(a) Find the values of a and b.

(b) Taking 2 cm to represent 1 unit on each axis, draw the graph $y = \frac{3(x - 1)(x + 2)}{x - 4}$ for $-5 \leqslant x \leqslant 2$.

(c) Use your graph to find the roots of the equation
$$\frac{3(x - 1)(x + 2)}{x - 4} = 1.$$

(d) By adding a suitable straight line to your graph, estimate the range of values of x for which $\frac{6x^2 + 6x - 12}{x - 4} \geqslant x + 1$.

(e) Estimate from your graph, the area bounded by the equation $= \frac{3(x - 1)(x + 2)}{x - 4}$ and the x-axis.

7. Answer this question on a sheet of graph paper.

(a) Given that $y = 2^x - 1$, copy and complete the following table.

x	-1	-0.5	0	0.5	1	2	3
y		-0.3			1	3	

(b) Using a scale of 4 cm to represent 1 unit on the x-axis, and 2 cm to represent 1 unit on the y-axis, draw the graph of $y = 2^x - 1$ for $-1 \leqslant x \leqslant 3$.

(c) Use your graph to solve the equation $2^x = 7$.

(d) On the same axis, draw the graph of the straight line $y = 2(1 - x)$. Write down the coordinates of the point where the graphs of $y = 2^x - 1$ and $y = 2(1 - x)$ meet.

(e) By drawing a tangent at the point where $x = 2$, find the gradient of the curve $y = 2^x - 1$ at the point (2, 3).

8. The diagram shows the speed-time graph of a car which uniformly accelerates from rest to 20 m/s in 10 seconds. The car then travels at this speed for 8 seconds before it decelerates at 1.6 m/s^2 until it comes to rest at t seconds. Calculate

(a) the acceleration of the car in the first 10 s,

(b) the distance travelled by the car in the first 18 s,

(c) the value of t.

9. The given graph shows the speed-time graph of a car. Given that the car travelled 20 km for the first 20 minutes, calculate

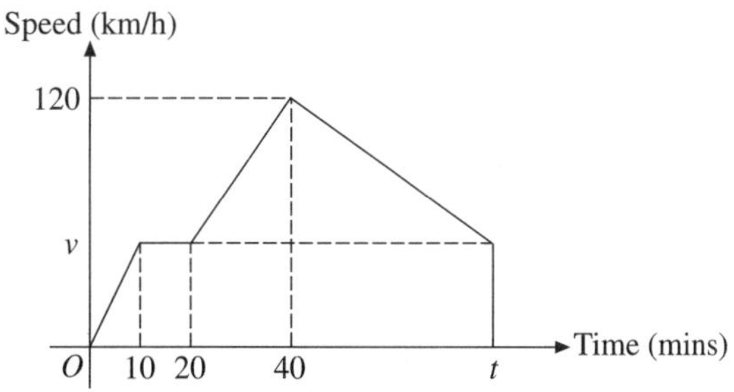

(a) the value of v,

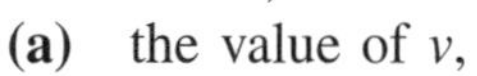

(b) the value of t if the retardation of the journey is 60 km/h^2,

(c) the speed of the car after an hour.

10. The diagram shows the speed-time graph of two cars A and B.

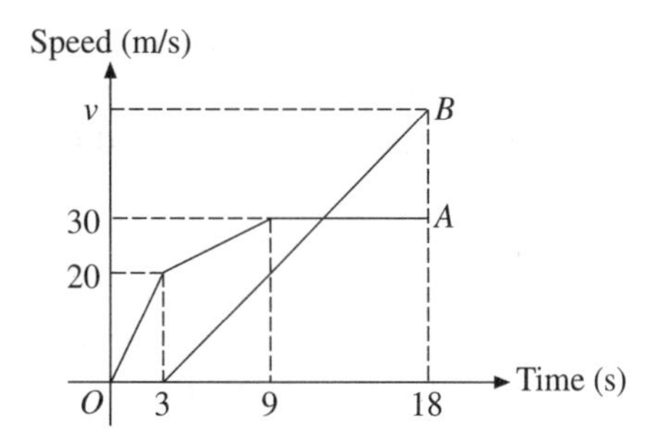

(a) Calculate the speed of the car A when $t = 6$ seconds.

(b) Calculate the total distance travelled by car A in 18 seconds.

(c) Given further that car B accelerates at 4.4 m/s^2, calculate the value of v.

(d) Calculate the distance between the two cars at $t = 18$ seconds.

5.9 Transformations

1.

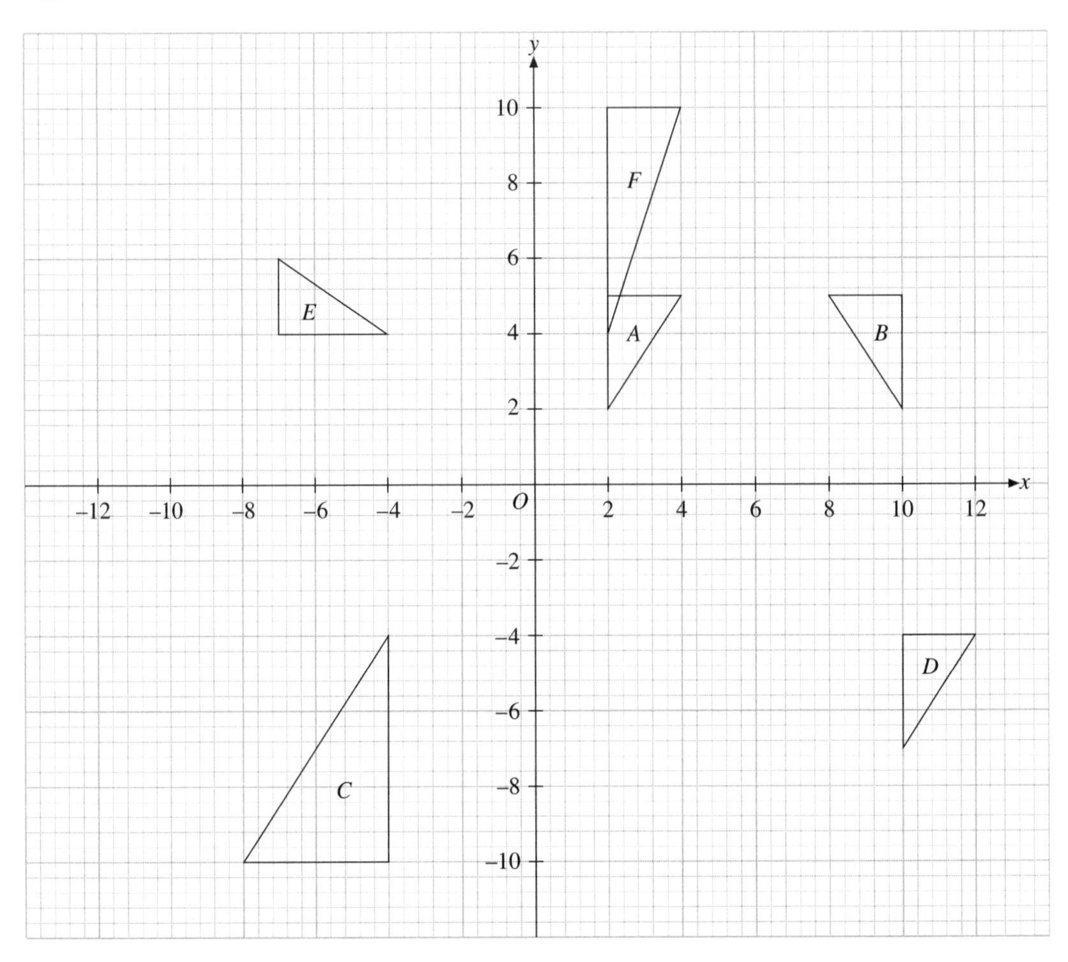

The diagram above shows triangles A, B, C, D, E and F.

(a) Triangle A is mapped onto triangle B by a reflection. Write down the equation of the line of reflection.

(b) Triangle A is mapped onto triangle C by an enlargement with centre (0, 0). Find the scale factor.

(c) Triangle A is mapped onto triangle D by a translation. Write down the column vector representing this translation.

(d) Triangle A is mapped onto triangle E by a single transformation. Describe fully this transformation.

(e) Triangle A is mapped onto triangle F by a single transformation. Describe fully this transformation.

2. Answer this question on a sheet of graph paper.

(a) Using a scale of 1 cm to represent 1 unit on each axis, draw x and y axes for $0 \leqslant x \leqslant 14$ and $-6 \leqslant y \leqslant 14$. Draw and label the rectangle whose vertices are $A(1, 2)$, $B(3, 2)$, $C(3, 3)$ and $D(1, 3)$.

(b) The enlargement E has the origin as its centre and maps rectangle $ABCD$ onto $A_1B_1C_1D_1$. Given that A_1 is the point (4, 8),

(i) draw and label the rectangle $A_1B_1C_1D_1$,

(ii) write down the scale factor of E.

(c) The point $C_2(7, -1)$ is the image of C under the reflection in the line m. Draw and label the line m and find the equation.

(d) The transformation R, a clockwise rotation of 90° about the origin, maps rectangle $ABCD$ onto rectangle $A_3B_3C_3D_3$. Draw and label rectangle $A_3B_3C_3D_3$.

3. Answer this question on a sheet of graph paper.
The vertices of triangle ABC are $A(2, 2)$, $B(5, 2)$ and $C(4, 4)$.

(a) Using a scale of 1 cm to represent 1 unit on both the x and y axes for $-6 \leqslant x \leqslant 10$ and $-6 \leqslant y \leqslant 10$, show and label triangle ABC.

(b) The point $P(0, 4)$ is the image of the point A under a reflection in the line l. Draw and label the line l and write down its equation.

(c) The transformation T is a translation represented by the column vector $\begin{pmatrix} -6 \\ 5 \end{pmatrix}$. Given that T maps $\triangle ABC$ onto $\triangle A_1B_1C_1$, draw and label $\triangle A_1B_1C_1$.

(d) The transformation R is 90° clockwise rotation about the origin. Given that R maps $\triangle ABC$ onto $\triangle A_2B_2C_2$, draw and label $\triangle A_2B_2C_2$.

(e) $\triangle ABC$ is mapped onto $\triangle A_3B_3C_3$ by a 180° rotation about the origin. Draw and label $\triangle A_3B_3C_3$.

(f) Given that $\triangle A_2B_2C_2$ is the image of $\triangle A_3B_3C_3$ under a single transformation H, describe H completely.

4. Answer this question on a sheet of graph paper.
The triangle ABC has vertices $A(-2, 0)$, $B(-5, -1)$ and $C(-4, -2)$. The triangle LMN has vertices $L(0, 6)$, $M(-1, 9)$ and $N(-2, 8)$. Using a scale of 1 cm to represent 1 unit on each axis, draw axes for x and y in the range $-6 \leqslant x \leqslant 10$ and $-4 \leqslant y \leqslant 9$. Draw and label triangle ABC and triangle LMN.

(a) Triangle ABC can be mapped onto triangle DEF by an enlargement, centre at the origin such that E is the point (10, 2).

(i) Draw and label triangle DEF.

(ii) Write down the scale factor of this enlargement.

(b) Triangle ABC can be mapped onto triangle LMN by rotation about the point (1, 0) followed by a translation.

(i) State the angle of rotation.

(ii) Write down the column vector of the translation.

(c) A transformation S which is such that (x, y) is mapped onto $(x + ky, y)$. S maps triangle ABC onto triangle AXY, where $X = (-3, -1)$.

(i) Find the value of k.

(ii) Draw and label triangle AXY.

(iii) Describe fully this transformation.

(d) Write down the numerical value of $\dfrac{\text{area of } \triangle DEF}{\text{area of } \triangle AXY}$.

5.

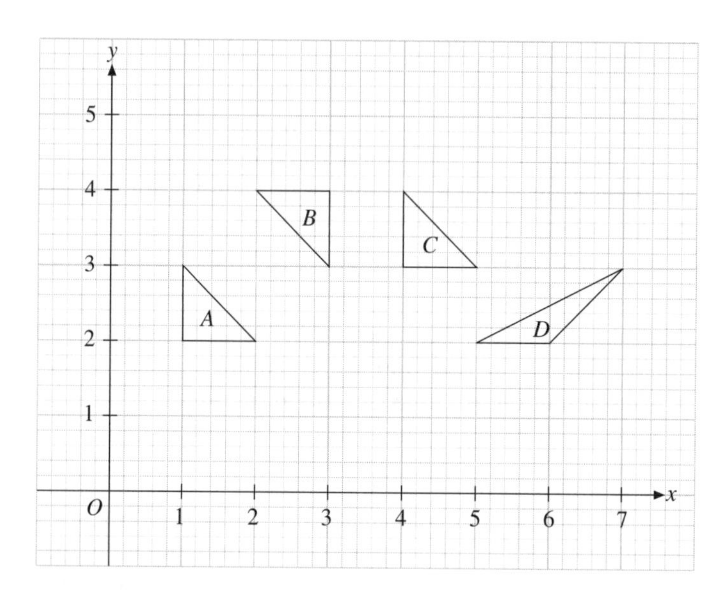

(a) A translation maps triangle A onto triangle C. Write down the column vector representing this translation.

(b) A reflection maps triangle A onto triangle B. Find the equation of the line in which triangle A is reflected.

(c) Describe completely the single transformation which maps triangle A onto triangle D.

6.

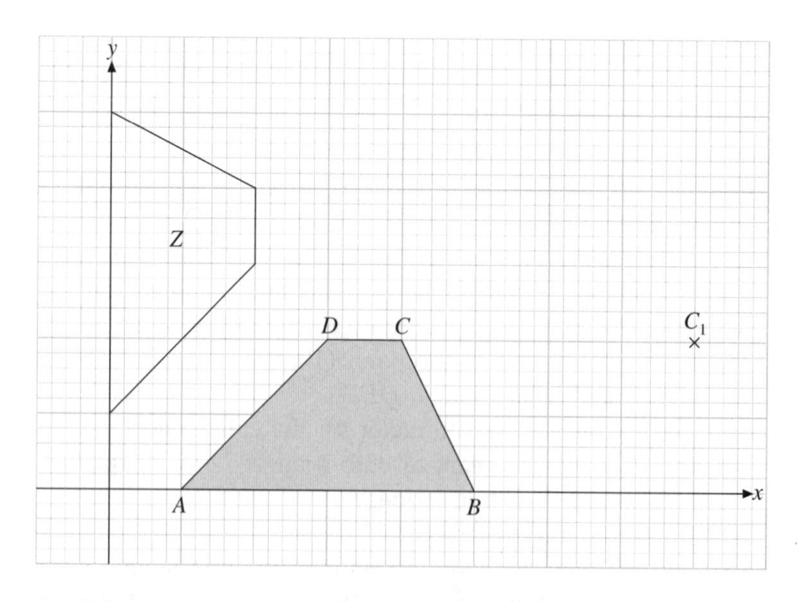

The diagram above shows the figure $ABCD$ and the point C_1. Draw and label on the same diagram,

(a) the image X, under a shear with the x-axis as the invariant line and which maps C to C_1,

(b) the image Y, under a rotation 90° about A in a clockwise direction,

(c) the line of reflection S, if Z is the image of figure $ABCD$ under a reflection.

7.

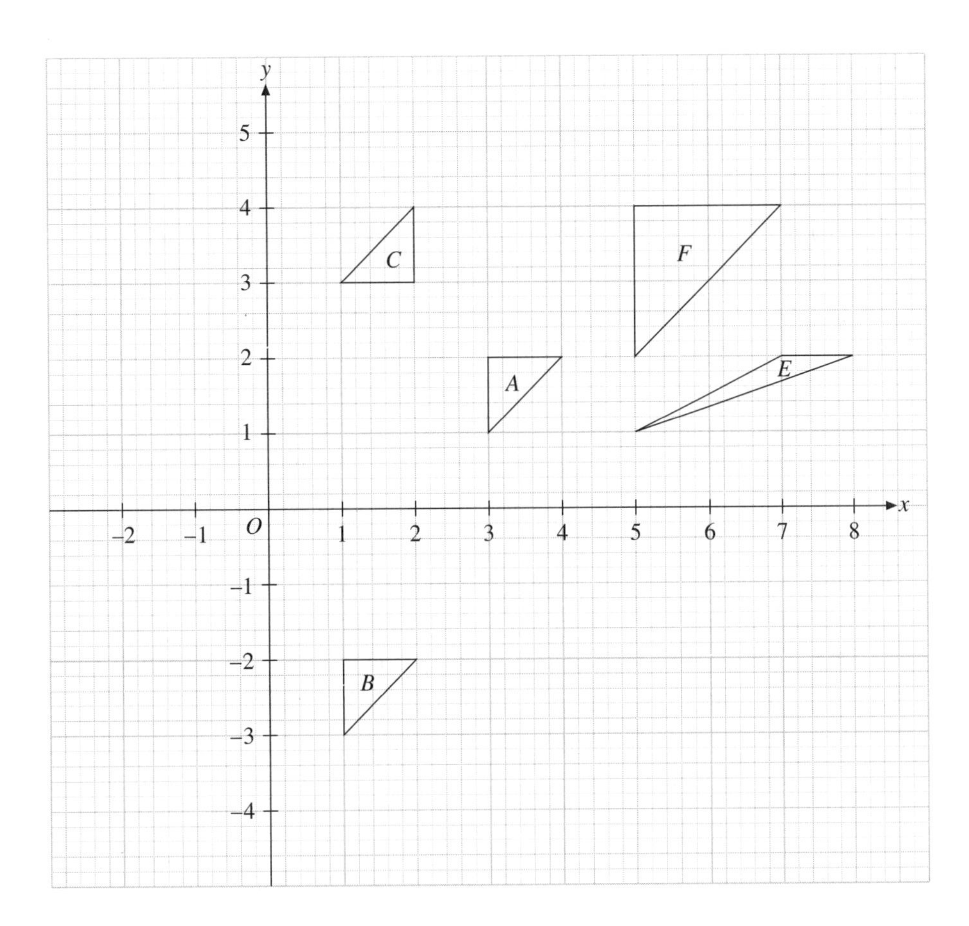

(a) A translation maps $\triangle A$ onto $\triangle B$. Find the column vector of this translation.

(b) A reflection maps $\triangle A$ onto $\triangle C$. Write down the equation of the axis of reflection.

(c) If $\triangle A$ is rotated 90° anticlockwise about (3, 0), draw and label its image $\triangle D$.

(d) If $\triangle A$ is mapped onto $\triangle E$ by a shear, describe the transformation fully.

(e) Describe the single transformation that mapped $\triangle A$ onto $\triangle F$.

8. A triangle ABC has vertices $A(2, 0)$, $B(4, -2)$ and $C(2, -4)$.

(a) Under an enlargement of scale factor $-\frac{1}{2}$ and $(0, -2)$ as the centre of enlargement, $\triangle ABC$ is mapped onto $\triangle A_1B_1C_1$. Draw and label $\triangle A_1B_1C_1$.

(b) A reflection in the line $y = -x$ maps $\triangle A_1B_1C_1$ onto $\triangle A_2B_2C_2$. Draw and label $\triangle A_2B_2C_2$.

(c) $\triangle A_2B_2C_2$ is then transformed into $\triangle A_3B_3C_3$ by a stretch with the x-axis as the invariant line and stretch factor 3. Draw and label $\triangle A_3B_3C_3$.

(d) State the coordinates of B_3.

9. Answer this question on a sheet of graph paper.
Using a scale of 2 cm to represent 1 unit on each axis, draw x and y axes for $-5 \leqslant x \leqslant 4$ and $-2 \leqslant y \leqslant 5$.

(a) Draw and label the square whose vertices are $A(1, 2)$, $B(2, 2)$, $C(2, 1)$ and $D(1, 1)$.

(b) Transformation P maps $ABCD$ onto square $FGCE$ with vertices $(4, -1)$, $(2, -1)$, $(2, 1)$ and $(4, 1)$. Describe P completely.

(c) Square $ABCD$ is mapped onto square $A_1B_1C_1D_1$ by an anticlockwise rotation through 90°. Given that A_1 is the point $(-1, 2)$, draw and label square $A_1B_1C_1D_1$. State the coordinates of the centre of rotation.

(d) The translation $\begin{pmatrix} -1 \\ 2 \end{pmatrix}$ maps square $A_1B_1C_1D_1$ onto square $A_2B_2C_2D_2$. Draw and label square $A_2B_2C_2D_2$.

(e) The transformation Q is such that it maps (x, y) onto $(x - 2\frac{1}{2}y, y)$. Given that Q maps $ABCD$ onto $A_3B_3C_3D_3$,

(i) find the coordinates of $A_3B_3C_3D_3$ and draw and label the figure,

(ii) describe fully the transformation Q.

10. Answer this question on a sheet of graph paper.
Using a scale of 1 cm to 1 unit on each axis, draw x and y axes for $-3 \leqslant x \leqslant 6$ and $-6 \leqslant y \leqslant 4$.

(a) The parallelogram $ABCD$ has vertices $A(0, 1)$, $B(1, 1)$, $C(2, 2)$ and $D(1, 2)$. Draw and label the parallelogram $ABCD$.

(b) The vertices of $A_1B_1C_1D_1$ are $A_1(-1, 0)$, $B_1(-1, -1)$, $C_1(-2, -2)$ and $D_1(-2, -1)$. Draw and label $A_1B_1C_1D_1$.
$ABCD$ is mapped onto the parallelogram $A_1B_1C_1D_1$ by a reflection in the line m. Draw and label the line m.

(c) $ABCD$ is mapped onto the parallelogram $A_2B_2C_2D_2$ by a rotation of 90° clockwise about the centre $(2, -2)$.

(i) Draw and label the parallelogram $A_2B_2C_2D_2$.

(ii) $A_1B_1C_1D_1$ can also be mapped onto $A_2B_2C_2D_2$ by a transformation. Describe fully this transformation.

(d) The points A and B are mapped onto $A_3(3, -5)$ and $B_3(1, -5)$ respectively by an enlargement. Find

(i) the coordinates of the centre of enlargement,

(ii) the scale factor.

(e) A shear S is such that it maps (x, y) onto $(x + 2y, y)$. Given that it maps A onto A_4,

(i) state the equation of the invariant line,

(ii) find the coordinates of A_4.

5.10 Statistics and Probability

1. A six-sided dice is thrown 29 times. The results are shown in the table below.

Number shown on dice	1	2	3	4	5	6
Frequency	8	7	5	2	3	4

(a) For these results, write down
 (i) the mode,
 (ii) the median.

(b) The dice is thrown one more time. Find the number shown on the dice if the mean of the 30 throws is to be exactly 3.

2.

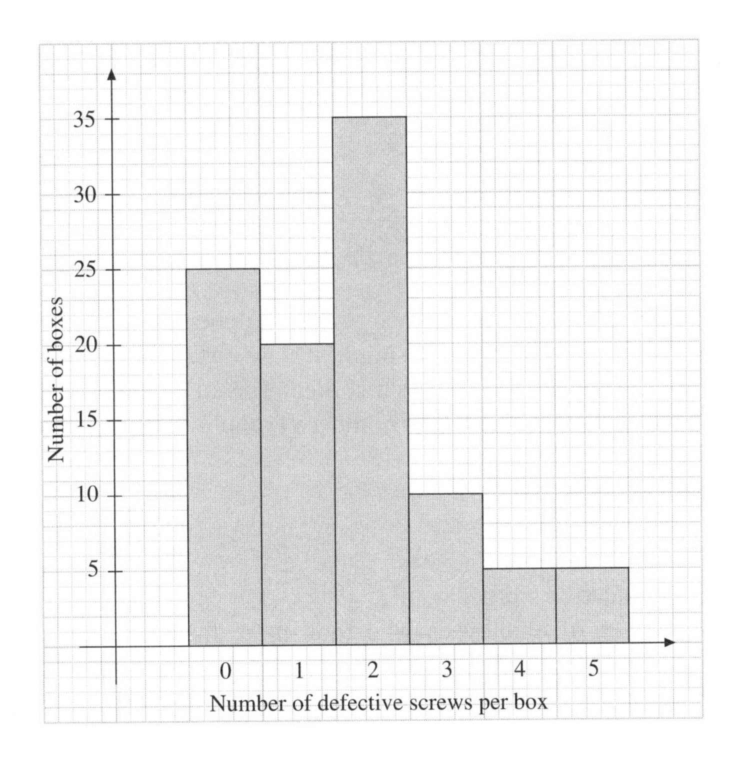

The histogram shows the number of defective screws per box for a sample of 100 boxes.

(a) Calculate the angle in a pie-chart, of the sector which represents boxes with 1 defective screw.

(b) Calculate the mean number of defective screws per box.

(c) Two boxes were chosen at random from the sample. Find the probability that both boxes will contain defective screws.

3.

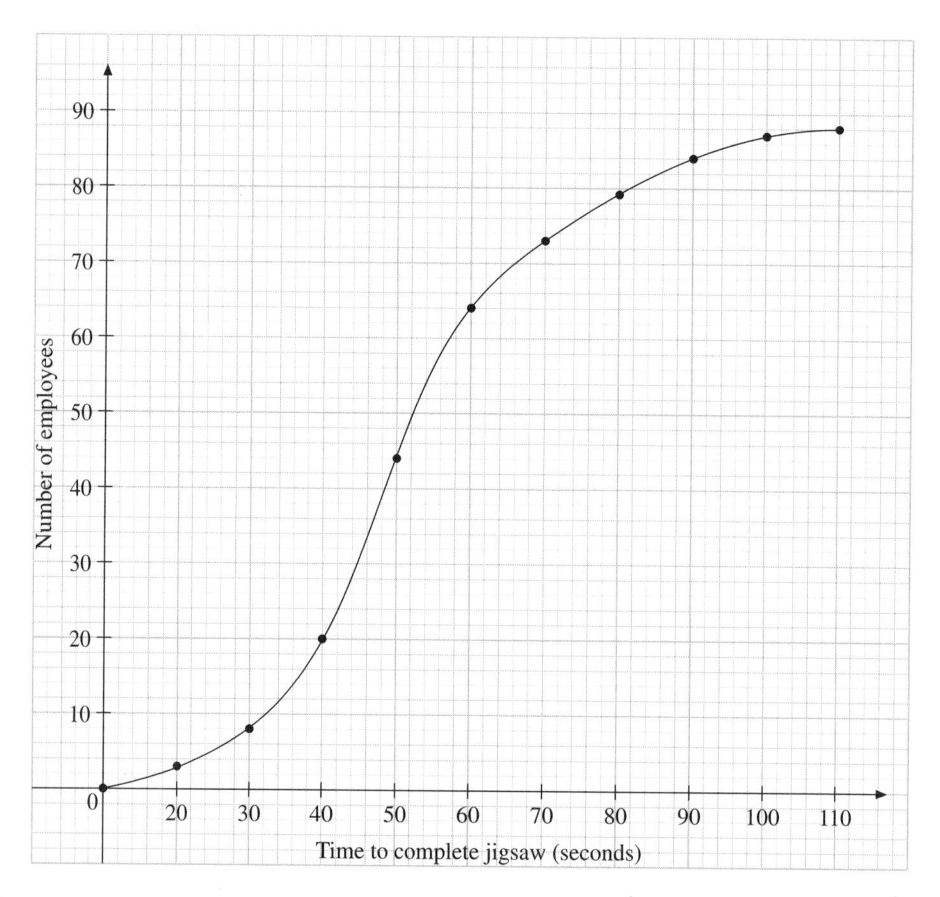

In an attempt to devise an aptitude test for applicants for assembly work, a firm gave each of its 88 employees a simple jigsaw puzzle to complete. The time taken to complete the jigsaw puzzle was recorded. The cumulative frequency curve below shows the time, t seconds, and the number of employees who took less than or equal to t seconds to complete the puzzle.

Use the curve to estimate

(a) the median time,

(b) the interquartile range,

(c) the number of employees who took more than 36 seconds to complete the puzzle,

(d) the probability that an employee chosen took less than or equal to 82 seconds to complete the puzzle.

4. (a) The cumulative distribution of marks gained by a group of 200 pupils in an examination is given in the table below.

Mark	10	20	30	40	50	60	70	80	90	100
No. of pupils scoring this mark or less	12	23	38	59	83	116	155	179	194	200

Using a vertical scale of 2 cm to represent 20 pupils and a horizontal scale of 2 cm to represent 10 marks, plot these values on graph paper and draw a smooth curve through your points. Use your graph to estimate

(i) the median mark,

(ii) the pass mark which will enable 65% of the pupils to pass.

(b) A circular board is divided into three sectors with angles of 180°, 120° and 60°, which are coloured red, green and white respectively.

(i) If a dart is thrown at random to hit the board, what is the probability that it will land in the green sector?

(ii) If 3 points are awarded for landing in the white sector, 2 for landing in the green sector and 1 for the red sector, what is the probability of scoring a total of 4 with two throws?

5. Answer this question on a sheet of graph paper.
The following tables gives a frequency distribution of the lengths of life (in arbitrary units) of 200 animals.

Length of life, x	$0 < x \leqslant 2$	$2 < x \leqslant 4$	$4 < x \leqslant 6$	$6 < x \leqslant 8$	$8 < x \leqslant 10$
No. of animals	15	47	50	35	24

Length of life, x	$10 < x \leqslant 12$	$12 < x \leqslant 14$	$14 < x \leqslant 16$	$16 < x \leqslant 18$
No. of animals	14	8	4	3

(a) Copy and complete the following table.

Length of life	2	4	6	8	10	12	14	16	18
No. of animals with less than or equal to this length of life	15	62	112						

(b) Using a horizontal scale of 1 cm to represent 1 unit of the length of life and a vertical scale of 1 cm to represent 10 animals, draw the cumulative frequency curve for the range $0 \leqslant x \leqslant 18$. Use your graph to estimate

(i) the median length of life,

(ii) the interquartile range.

(c) If one animal is selected at random, find, as a fraction in its lowest term, the probability that its length of life is

(i) greater than 12 units,

(ii) either not greater than 4 units or greater than 16 units.

6. Five discs numbered 1 to 5 are placed in a bag. A disc is drawn out of the bag at random. Without putting the first disc back into the bag, a second disc is drawn.

(a) Complete the probability tree. (O = odd number, E = even number)

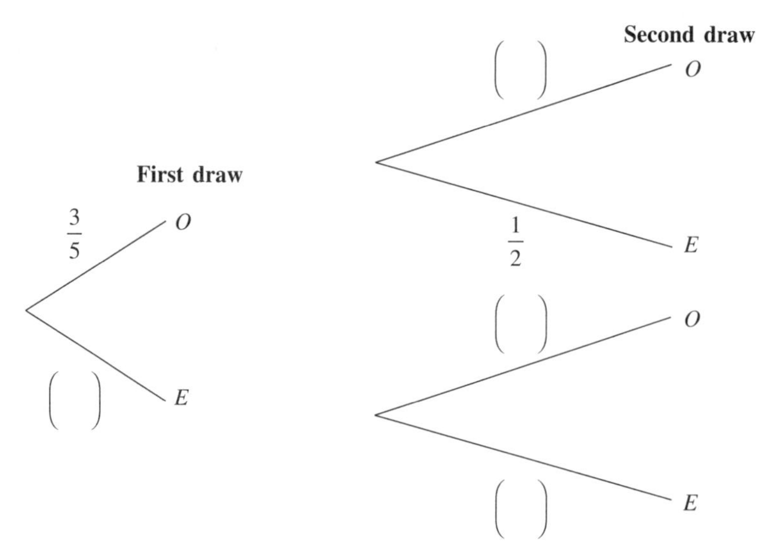

(b) Write down the probability that the second disc is even given that the first one drawn is also even.

(c) Find the probability that one disc is odd while the other is even.

(d) Find the probability that both numbers drawn are greater than 3.

7. A bag contains 3 red balls, 4 blue balls and 5 yellow balls.

(a) Three balls are drawn from the bag without replacement.

(i) If the first ball drawn is yellow, what is the probability that the second ball drawn is also yellow?

(ii) If the first ball drawn is yellow, the second is red, what is the probability that the third is blue?

(iii) What is the probability that all three red balls are drawn?

(b) If eight balls are drawn from the bag without replacement, what is the probability that at least one of the balls is yellow?

8. A certain brand of boxes of matches is advertised as having 'average content 50 matches'. The probability that a box chosen at random will contain exactly 50 matches is $\frac{5}{8}$.

(a) Calculate the probability that a box of matches chosen at random will not contain exactly 50 matches.

The probability that a box chosen at random will contain more than 50 matches is twice the probability that it will contain less than 50 matches.

(b) Calculate the probability that

(i) one box chosen at random will contain at least 50 matches,

(ii) of two boxes chosen at random, at least one will contain less than 50 matches.

9. From a starting point O in a school field a boy walks a sequence of stages, each 1 km either due north or due east. The direction of each stage is decided by tossing an unbiased coin. If it is 'Heads', he will go North. If it is 'Tails', he will go East.

(a) How many different routes are possible from O to

(i) R,

(ii) S,

(iii) C.

(b) P(A) denotes the probability that, after four stages, the boy will be at A, and so on. Calculate

(i) P(A), **(ii)** P(B),

(iii) P(C), **(iv)** P(D),

(v) P(E), **(vi)** P(R).

(c) What is the probability that the boy ends up more than 3 km from O after four stages?

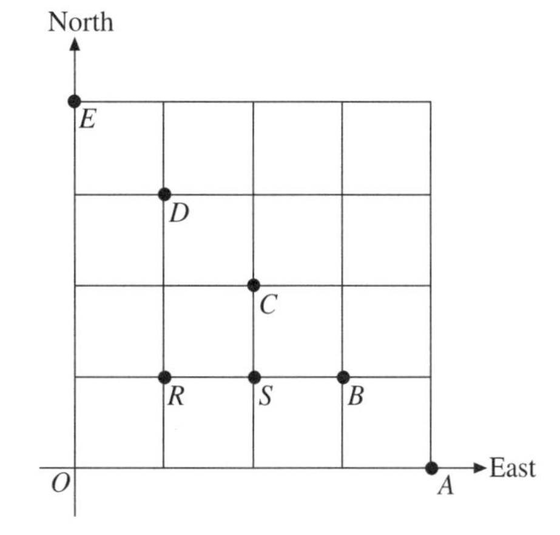

10. Each of two boxes contains five balls labelled 1, 2, 3, 4 and 5. One ball is removed at random from each box and the difference of the resulting numbers is shown in the possibility diagram.

–	1	2	3	4	5
1	0		2		
2					3
3					
4			1		
5	4				

(a) Copy and complete the possibility diagram.

(b) Using the diagram, find the probability that the difference of the two numbers is

(i) an even number,

(ii) a prime number.

ASSESSMENT PAPER SET A (PAPER 1)

Time : $2\frac{1}{2}$ hours
Marks: 100

Answer *all* questions.
Write your answers in the spaces provided on the question paper.
If working is needed for any question, show it in the space below that question.
Omission of essential working will result in loss of marks.
No calculators may be used in this paper.
The number of marks is given in brackets [ ] at the end of each part question.
This paper consists of 28 questions.

1. Calculate the exact value of

(a) $6.4 - 2\frac{2}{3}$, [1]

(b) $\frac{0.888 \times 99.9}{0.003\ 33}$, [1]

(c) $\frac{(0.4)^2}{\sqrt[3]{0.064}}$. [1]

Ans (a) ____________________

(b) ____________________

(c) ____________________

2. Factorise completely

(a) $27x^2 - 12x$, [1]

(b) $9 - 16y^{16}$, [1]

(c) $w^2 - 10w - 24$. [1]

Ans (a) ____________________

(b) ____________________

(c) ____________________

3.

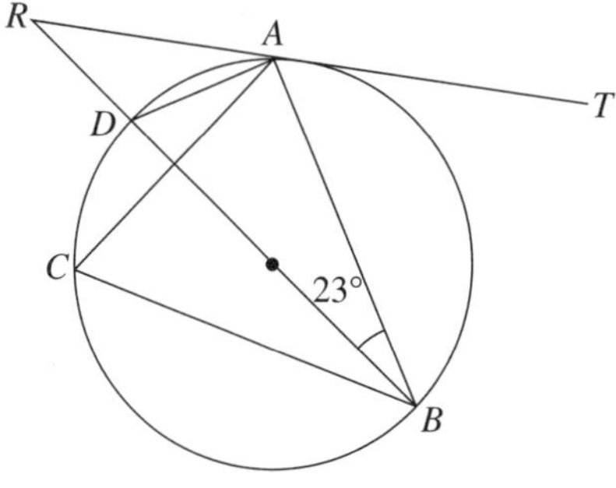

BD is the diameter of a circle. RAT is a tangent to the circle at A. Given that $A\hat{B}D = 23°$, calculate

(a) $D\hat{A}R$, [1]

(b) $D\hat{R}A$, [1]

(c) $A\hat{C}B$. [1]

Ans (a) ____________________

(b) ____________________

(c) ____________________

4. **(a)** Given that y varies as the square of x and that $y = 24$ when $x = 9$, express y in terms of x. [1]

(b) Hence, find the value of

(i) x when $y = 44$, [1]

(ii) y when $x = 0.16$. [1]

Ans (a) ____________________

(b) (i) ____________________

(ii) ____________________

5. Bottle A contains 68 ml of water. Bottle B contains 51 ml of water. Bottle C contains 22 ml of water. If all measurements are measured correct to 2 significant figures, find

(a) the least possible sum of the volumes of water in bottle A and bottle B, [1]

(b) the greatest possible difference in the volumes of water in bottle B and bottle C, [1]

(c) the least possible ratio of the volume of water in bottle A to the volume of water in bottle C. [1]

Ans (a) ____________________

(b) ____________________

(c) ____________________

6. Solve the simultaneous equations.

$$y = \frac{1}{3}x$$
$$3x - 2y = 14$$

[3]

Ans ____________________

7. (a) Given that $1\frac{1}{4} : x = 15 : 2$, find the value of x. [1]

(b) 15 taps could fill a tank completely with water in 1 hour. If the number of taps were to increase by 3, how many minutes would it take to fill the same tank completely with water? [2]

Ans (a) ____________________

(b) ____________________

8. Find the values of

(a) $\left(1\frac{1}{2}\right)^{-4}$, [1]

(b) $4^{1.5}$, [1]

(c) $19^{94} \div 19^{93}$. [1]

Ans (a) ______________________

(b) ______________________

(c) ______________________

9. Solve the equations.

(a) $4 + 2(x - 3) = 13 - 3x$ [1]

(b) $(1 - 2y)^2 = 121$ [2]

Ans (a) ______________________

(b) ______________________

10. The bar chart shows the number of books read by the pupils of a class in a certain month.

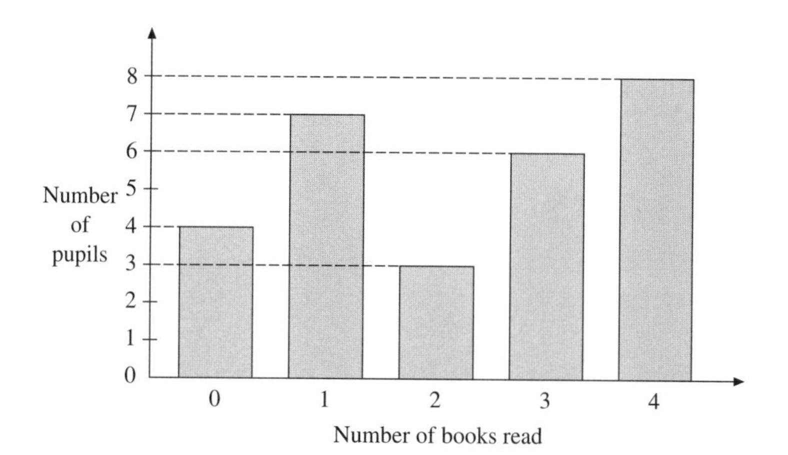

Find

(a) the mode of the distribution, [1]

(b) the total number of pupils in the class, [1]

(c) the mean number of books read by a pupil in the class. [1]

Ans (a) ______________________

(b) ______________________

(c) ______________________

11. **(a)** Arrange the following in descending order.

$$\frac{7}{16}, \frac{4}{9}, 0.4, 43\% \qquad [1]$$

(b) Find the integer values of x which satisfy all three conditions.

$$1 - 2x \leqslant 9, x \quad -3, \quad x < 1 \qquad [2]$$

Ans (a) 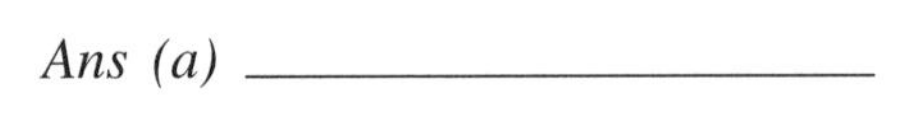

(b) ______________________

12.

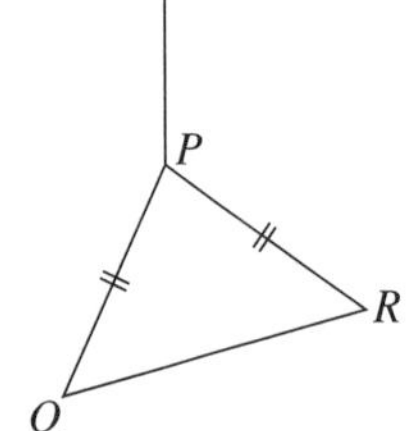

Three points P, Q and R are such that the bearing of R from P is 125°, the bearing of Q from P is 205°, and $PQ = PR$. Calculate

(a) the bearing of P from R, [1]

(b) the bearing of P from Q, [1]

(c) the bearing of R from Q. [1]

Ans (a) ______________________

(b) ______________________

(c) ______________________

13. A swimming pool is 40 m wide and 2 m deep. A model of the pool has a depth of 0.8 cm.

(a) Calculate the width of the model. [1]

(b) If the pool can hold 800 m^3 of water, how many cubic centimetres of water would the model of the pool hold? [2]

Ans (a) ____________________

(b) ____________________

14. *OABC* is a quadrant of a circle of radius 7 cm. Calculate

(a) the area of the triangle *OAC*, [1]

(b) the shaded area, taking π to be $\frac{22}{7}$. [2]

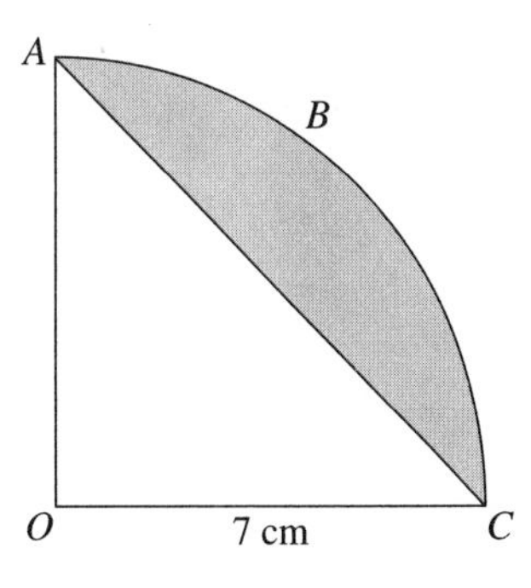

Ans (a) ____________________

(b) ____________________

15. **(a)** Express $0.002 + 1.41 \times 10^{-2}$ in standard form. [1]

(b) Given that $x = 3 \times 10^{-5}$, express $\frac{1}{12}x^2$ in standard form. [2]

Ans (a) ____________________

(b) ____________________

16. Three angles of a heptagon are in the ratio 2 : 3 : 5 while the remaining angles are all 120° each. Find the sizes of the three angles. [3]

Ans ____________________

____

____

17. 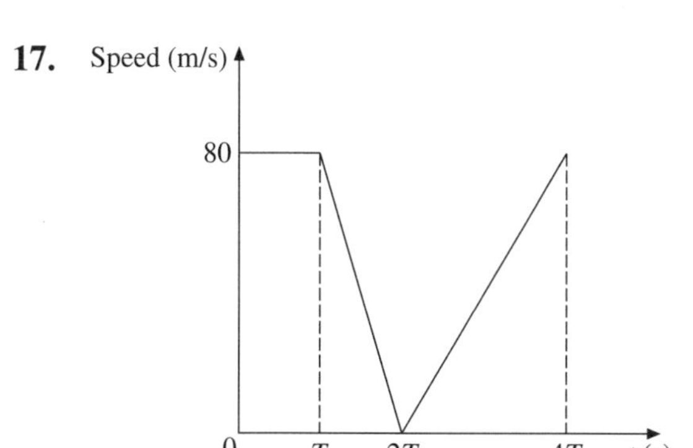

The diagram shows the speed-time graph of a particle between $t = 0$ and $t = 4T$. If the total distance travelled is 400 m, find

(a) the value of T, [2]

(b) the retardation during the motion. [1]

Ans (a) ____________________

(b) ____________________

18. (a) A box contains forty 10¢ coins and some 5¢ coins which can be exchanged for fifteen 20¢ coins and five 50¢ coins. Find the number of 5¢ coins in the box. [2]

(b) 1 000 sweets are to be shared among 3 boys. Boy A gets 60% and boy B gets 50% of what A gets. What percentage of the sweets does C get? [2]

Ans (a) ____________________

(b) ____________________

19.

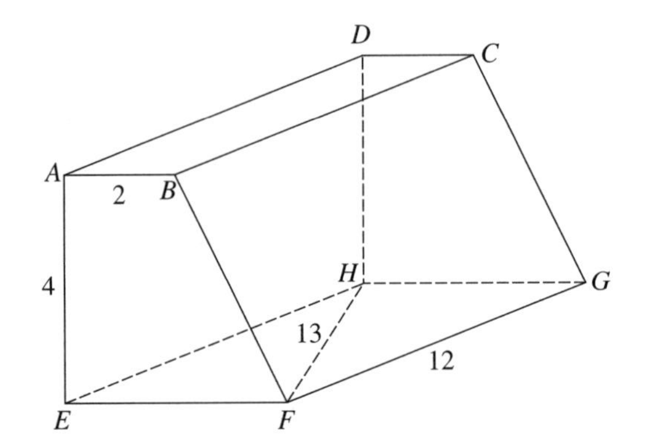

ABCDEFGH is a right prism. *ABFE* is a trapezium. $AB = 2$ cm, $AE = 4$ cm, $FG = 12$ cm and $FH = 13$ cm. Calculate

(a) the tangent of the angle of elevation of *D* from *F*, [1]

(b) *EF*, [1]

(c) the volume of the prism. [2]

Ans (a) ________________

(b) ________________

(c) ________________

20.

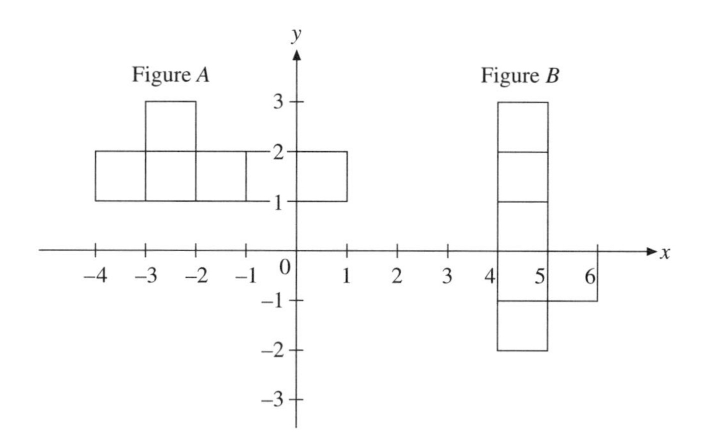

(a) **(i)** Add one square to figure A above to make a figure which has line symmetry. [1]

(ii) Write down the equation of the line of symmetry. [1]

(b) **(i)** Add one square to figure B above to make a figure which has rotational symmetry. [1]

(ii) Write down the coordinates of the centre of rotational symmetry. [1]

Ans (a) (ii) ____________________

(b) (ii) ____________________

21. On the axes below, sketch the graphs of

(a) $x + y = 0$,

Ans (a)

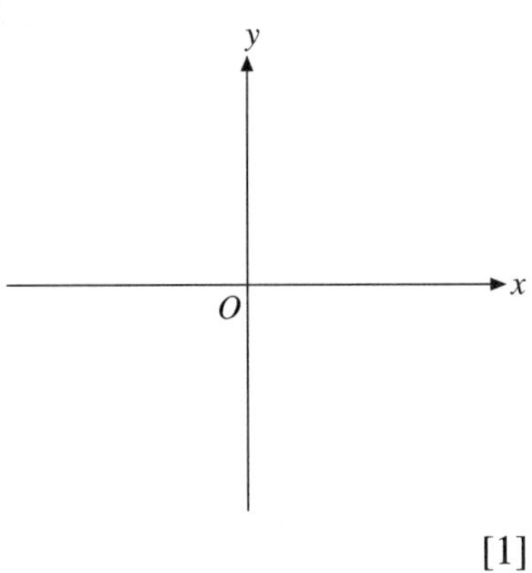

[1]

(b) $x^3 + y = 0$,

Ans (b)

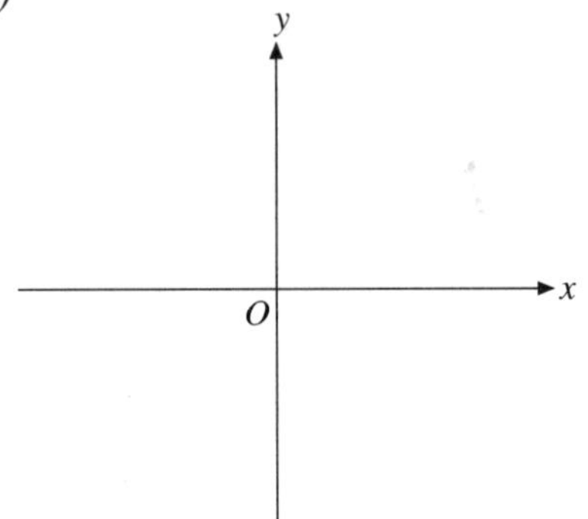

[1]

(c) $xy = 1$.

Ans (c)

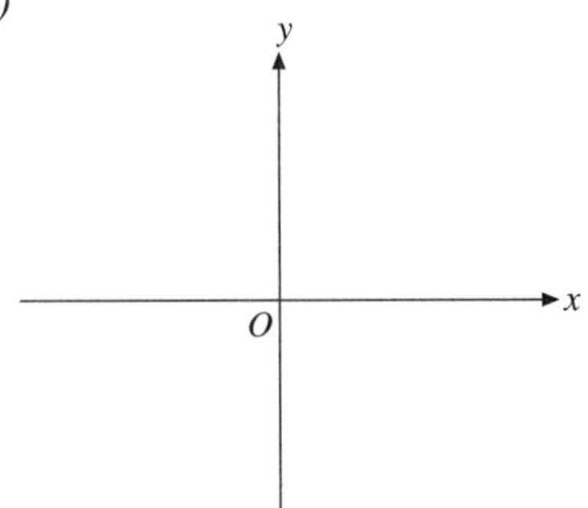

[2]

22. $ABCD$ is a square of side 5 cm. Indicate in the square,

(a) the locus of points which are equidistant from A and B,

(b) the locus of points which are 5 cm from C,

(c) the region in which the point X must lie if $AX \leqslant BC$ and $CX \geqslant 5$ cm. [4]

Ans

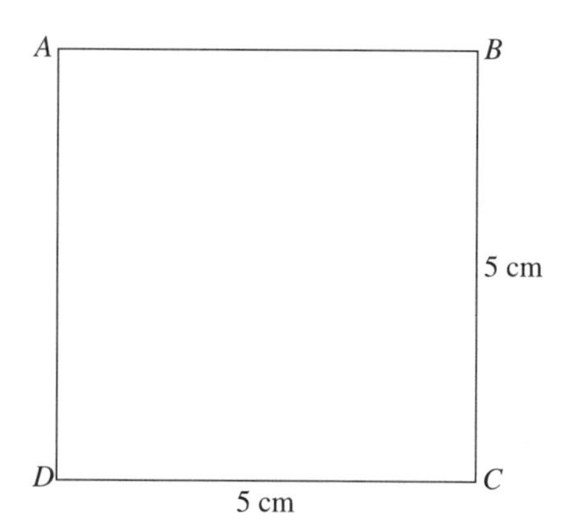

23. A bag contains 96 balls of equal size of which x are red, 20 are white and the rest are blue.

(a) A ball is drawn at random from the bag. If the probability that this ball is red is $\frac{1}{4}$, find x. [1]

(b) State, as a fraction in its lowest term, the probability that a ball drawn at random is not white. [1]

(c) A ball is drawn at random and is not replaced. A second ball is then drawn. Find, as a fraction in its lowest term, the probability that the first ball is white and the second is blue. [2]

Ans (a) ____________________

(b) ____________________

(c) ____________________

24. **(a)** Complete the following table.

Series	No. of terms (N)	Total (T)
1	1	1
1 + 3	2	4
1 + 3 + 5	3	9
1 + 3 + 5 + 7		
1 + 3 + 5 + 7 + 9		

[1]

(b) By using the variables N and T, state a rule to calculate the total sum without actually adding up the terms. [1]

(c) Hence, evaluate

(i) $1 + 3 + 5 + 7 + 9 + 11 + 13 + 15 + 17 + 19 + 21$, [1]

(ii) $1 + 3 + 5 + \ldots + 47 + 49$. [1]

Ans (b) ________________

(c) (i) ________________

(ii) ________________

25. O is the origin, X is the point (3, 8), Y is the point (1, 5). The directed line segments $\overrightarrow{OX}$ and $\overrightarrow{OY}$ represent vectors $\mathbf{x}$ and $\mathbf{y}$ respectively.

(a) Find $|\mathbf{x}|$. [1]

(b) Given that P is the point (a, b) and that $\overrightarrow{OP} = \mathbf{x} + 3\mathbf{y}$, find the values of a and b. [2]

(c) Given also that Q is the point (c, d) and that $\overrightarrow{QP} = 2\mathbf{x} - \mathbf{y}$, find the values of c and d. [2]

Ans (a) ____________________

(b) ____________________

(c) ____________________

26. In a survey, 30 pupils were asked how long it took them to solve a Mathematics problem. The pupils were divided into four groups:

A: those who took less than 1 minute,

B: those who took at least 1 minute, but less than 2 minutes,

C: those who took at least 2 minutes, but less than 3 minutes,

D: those who took at least 3 minutes, but less than 5 minutes.

Each of the pupils is in one of the four groups, as shown on the given pie-chart.

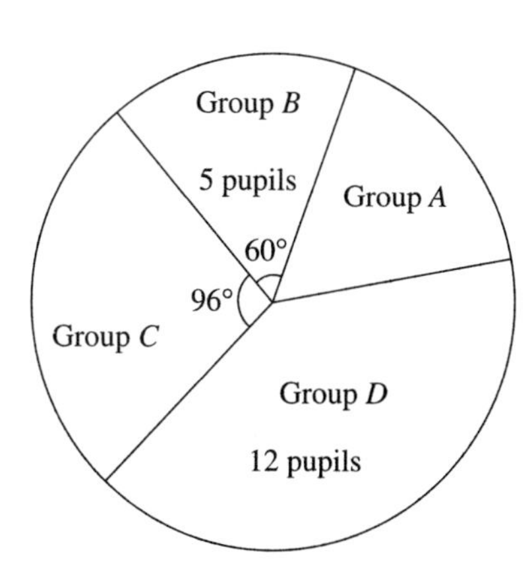

(a) Calculate the angle of the sector which represents the pupils in group D. [1]

Ans (a) ____________________

(b) Complete the table below. [2]

Ans (b)

	Group A	**Group B**	**Group C**	**Group D**
Time (t minutes)	$0 \leqslant t < 1$	$1 \leqslant t < 2$	$2 \leqslant t < 3$	$3 \leqslant t < 5$
No. of pupils		5		12

(c) The information can also be represented in a histogram. Complete the histogram. [2]

Ans (c)

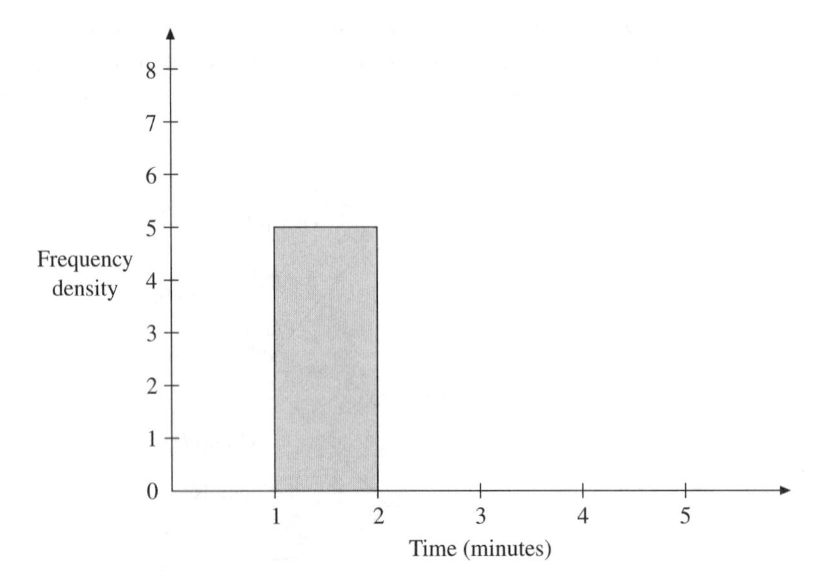

27. Find the coordinates of the image of the point (3, 0) under a reflection

(a) in the y-axis, [1]

(b) in the line $x = 5$, [2]

(c) in the line $y = x$. [2]

Ans (a) ______________________

(b) ______________________

(c) ______________________

28. **(a)** Points P, Q and R have coordinates (3, 1), (–9, 4) and (–1, k). Find the value of k such that P, Q and R all lie on the same straight line. [2]

(b) $ABCD$ is a parallelogram. Given that the equation of AB is $y = \frac{x}{k} + k$, B is (k, 10) and C is (8, 6), find

(i) the value of k and state the gradient of AB, [2]

(ii) the equation of CD. [2]

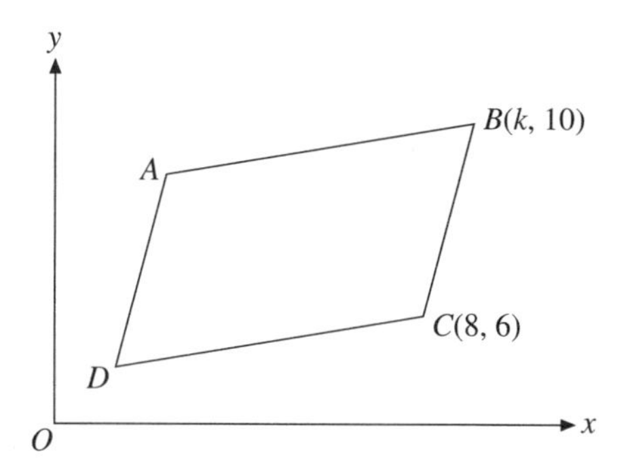

Ans (a) ______________________

(b) (i) ______________________

(ii) ______________________

ASSESSMENT PAPER SET A (PAPER 2)

Time : $2\frac{1}{2}$ hours
Marks: 100

This paper consists of 2 sections.
Section A consists of **5 questions**.
Section B consists of **7 questions**.
Calculators may be used in this paper. If the degree of accuracy is not specified and if the answer is not exact, the answer should be given to three significant figures.

Section A (52 marks)
ALL *questions may be attempted.*

1.

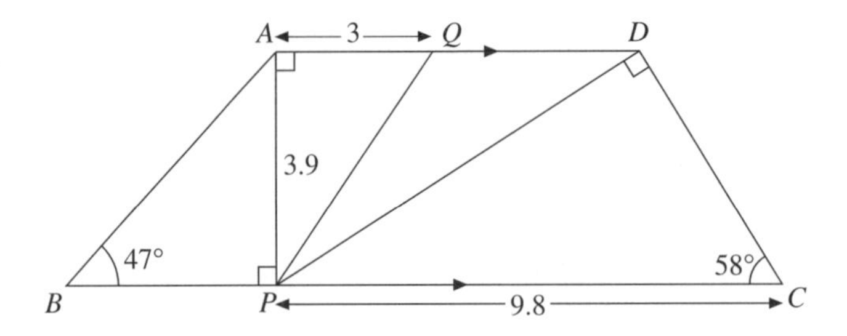

In the diagram, $AQ = 3$ cm, $AP = 3.9$ cm, $CP = 9.8$ cm, $A\hat{B}P = 47°$, $D\hat{C}P = 58°$, $A\hat{P}B = P\hat{A}Q = C\hat{D}P = 90°$ and $AD \,//\, BC$. Calculate

(a) AB, [3]
(b) CD, [2]
(c) $Q\hat{P}D$. [3]

2. **(a)** Solve the equation $\frac{4}{w+3} = 5w$. [4]

(b) Express $\frac{6}{2x-3} - \frac{5}{x}$ as a single fraction. [3]

(c) Simplify $\frac{8x + 6x^2y}{3x^2y^2 - 5xy - 12}$. [3]

(d) Given that $q = \frac{3(q-r)}{3q-r}$, make r the subject. [3]

3. **(a)** In the first six months of 1999, a motorist recorded that he had driven 1 980 km, 2 392 km, 2 171 km, 1 620 km, 3 600 km and 2 900 km. Calculate

(i) the average monthly distance travelled, [1]

(ii) the fuel bill for the six months if the car uses petrol costing \$1.15 per litre, at an average rate of 8.7 litres per 100 km. [3]

(b)

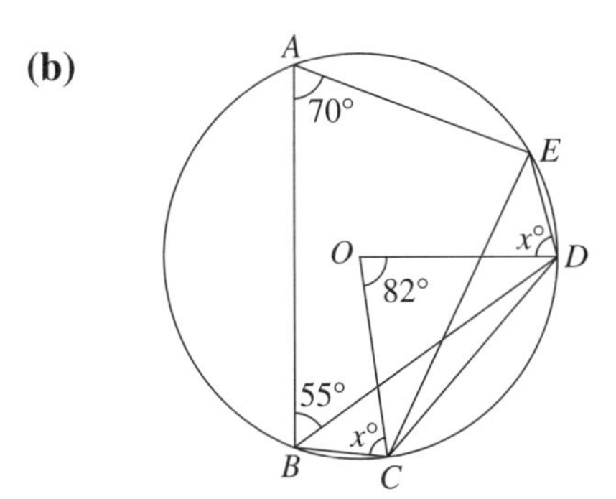

O is the centre of the circle through A, B, C, D and E. $C\hat{O}D = 82°$, $A\hat{B}D = 55°$, $B\hat{A}E = 70°$ and $B\hat{C}O = E\hat{D}O = x°$. Calculate

(i) the sum of interior angles of the pentagon $ABCDE$, [2]

(ii) $O\hat{D}C$, [1]

(iii) $C\hat{E}D$, [1]

(iv) $A\hat{E}C$, [2]

(v) x. [2]

4. **(a)** The vectors **r** and **s** are defined by $\mathbf{r} = \begin{pmatrix} 3 \\ 5 \end{pmatrix}$ and $\mathbf{s} = \begin{pmatrix} -4 \\ 7 \end{pmatrix}$.

(i) Evaluate $|\mathbf{s}|$. [1]

(ii) If $3\mathbf{r} - 2\mathbf{t} = 5\mathbf{s}$, express **t** as a column vector. [2]

(b) In the diagram, $ABCD$ is a parallelogram. AD and DT are straight lines. $BS = 2$ cm and $AD = 6$ cm. Find the numerical value of

(i) $\dfrac{AB}{AT}$, [2]

(ii) $\dfrac{\text{area of } \triangle BST}{\text{area of } \triangle CSD}$, [2]

(iii) $\dfrac{\text{area of } \triangle TBS}{\text{area of } \triangle TAD}$. [2]

(c) Given that area of $\triangle BST = 3$ cm^2, find the area of parallelogram $ABCD$. [3]

5. Mr Ang had \$38 125 as his savings.

(a) He spent 8% of his money on a new computer. How much did he spend on the computer? [2]

(b) He deposited \$15 000 from his savings into a bank at a compound interest of 4% per annum. Calculate the amount he had with the bank at the end of three years. (Correct your answer to the nearest dollars.) [3]

(c) He sold his computer at a loss of 40%. Find the amount for which he sold his computer. [2]

Section B (48 marks)
Answer **four** questions in this section.
Each question in this section carries 12 marks.

6.

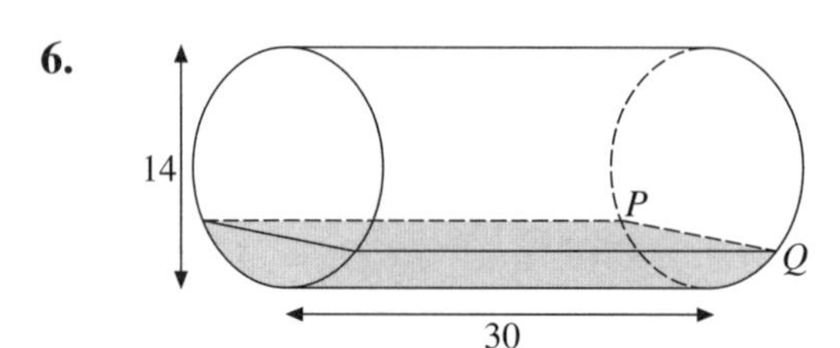

Figure I

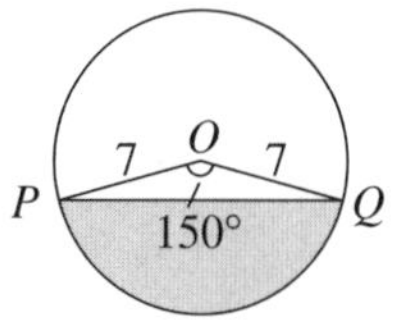

Figure II

In this question, take π to be $\frac{22}{7}$.

Figure I shows a solid cylinder of diameter 14 cm and length 30 cm. The shaded portion is made of lead, while the unshaded portion is made of wood.

Figure II shows a circular end of the cylinder, O is the centre of the circle, the chord PQ represents the surface of the lead portion and $P\hat{O}Q = 150°$. Calculate

(a) the length of the arc PQ, [2]

(b) the area of the sector OPQ, [2]

(c) the area of the shaded segment, [3]

(d) the volume of the lead portion, [1]

(e) the volume of the cylinder, [2]

(f) the weight of the cylinder, given that the densities of lead and wood are 12.7 g/cm^3 and 1.21 g/cm^3 respectively. Give your answer in kilograms, correct to 1 decimal place. [2]

7. (a) At a garden centre, a shrub and a tree cost $140 altogether. Four shrubs and nine trees cost $1 000. Find the cost of a shrub and the cost of a tree. [4]

(b) At another garden centre, a shrub and a tree also cost $140 altogether. Mrs Wong decides to spend $1 000 on shrubs and trees from this garden centre. If she spends all the money on shrubs alone, she could buy 15 more items than she could if she spends all the money on trees. Taking the cost of a shrub to be $$s$, write down an expression in terms of s for

(i) the cost of a tree,

(ii) the number of trees which could be bought for $1 000.

Write down an equation which s must satisfy and show that it reduces to $3s^2 - 820s + 28\ 000 = 0$.

Solve this equation and state the cost of a shrub and the cost of a tree at this garden centre. [8]

8.

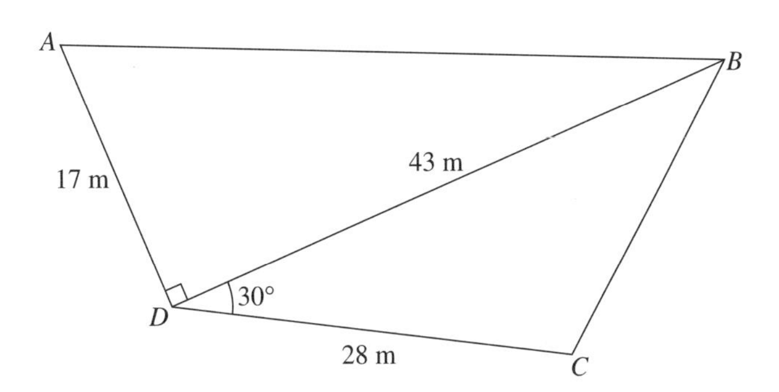

A, B, C and D are four points on level ground. A is due north of D, B is due east of D and $B\hat{D}C = 30°$. The distance $AD = 17$ m, $BD = 43$ m and $CD = 28$ m. Calculate

(a) $B\hat{A}D$, [2]

(b) the bearing of B from A, [1]

(c) the area of $\triangle BCD$, [2]

(d) the distance BC, [2]

(e) the perimeter of $ABCD$, [3]

(f) the area of $ABCD$. [2]

9. The square $ABCD$ has vertices $A(3, 2)$, $B(5, 2)$, $C(5, 4)$ and $D(3, 4)$.
The square $EFGH$ has vertices $E(6, -1)$, $F(2, -1)$, $G(2, -5)$ and $H(6, -5)$.
The square $KLMN$ has vertices $K(-3, 4)$, $L(-3, 6)$ $M(-5, 6)$ and $N(-5, 4)$.

(a) Draw these squares on graph paper, using a scale of 1 cm to represent 1 unit on each axis, for $-6 \leqslant x \leqslant 12$ and $-6 \leqslant y \leqslant 6$, labelling the vertices clearly. [3]

(b) The square $ABCD$ is mapped onto the square $EFGH$ by an enlargement.

(i) Write down the coordinates of the centre of the enlargement. [2]

(ii) Write down the scale factor of the enlargement. [1]

(iii) Find the value of the ratio

$$\frac{\text{area of square } ABCD}{\text{area of square } EFGH},$$

expressing your answer in its lowest term. [2]

(c) The square $ABCD$ is mapped onto the square $KLMN$ by a reflection in the line m, followed by a reflection in the x-axis.

(i) Draw the line m on your graph and label it clearly. [1]

(ii) Find the equation of the line m. [2]

(iii) Describe a single transformation which maps the square $ABCD$ onto the square $KLMN$. [1]

10. The variables x and y are connected by the equation

$$y = \frac{1}{5}x(x^2 - 11).$$

Some corresponding values of x and y, corrected to 1 decimal place where necessary, are given in the table.

x	–3.5	–3	–2.5	–2	–1.5	–1	–0.5	0	0.5	1	1.5	2	2.5	3	3.5
y	–0.9	1.2	2.4	2.8	a	2	1.1	0	–1.1	–2	b	–2.8	–2.4	–1.2	0.9

(a) Calculate the value of a and of b, giving your answer correct to 1 decimal place. [2]

(b) Taking 2 cm to represent 1 unit on each axis, draw the graph of $y = \frac{1}{5}x(x^2 - 11)$ for the values of x in the range $-3.5 \leqslant x \leqslant 3.5$. [4]

(c) Use your graph to estimate the solutions of the equation $x^3 - 11x = 8$ in the range $-3.5 \leqslant x \leqslant 3.5$. [3]

(d) Using your graph, write down the range of values of x for which

(i) the gradient of the curve is negative, [1]

(ii) $\frac{1}{5}x(x^2 - 11) > 0$. [2]

11.

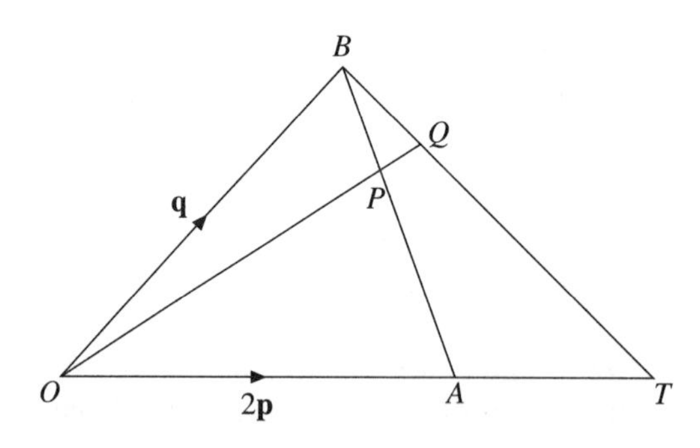

In the diagram, $\overrightarrow{OA} = 2\mathbf{p}$, $\overrightarrow{OB} = \mathbf{q}$, $\overrightarrow{OA} = 2\overrightarrow{AT}$ and $\overrightarrow{BT} = 4\overrightarrow{BQ}$. The lines OQ and AB intersect at P.

(a) Express, as simply as possible in terms of $\mathbf{p}$ and/or $\mathbf{q}$

(i) $\overrightarrow{OT}$, [1]

(ii) $\overrightarrow{BT}$, [1]

(iii) $\overrightarrow{AB}$, [1]

(iv) $\overrightarrow{OQ}$. [1]

(b) **(i)** Given that $\overrightarrow{AP} = h\overrightarrow{AB}$, express $\overrightarrow{AP}$ in terms of $\mathbf{p}$, $\mathbf{q}$ and h. [1]

(ii) Hence, show that $\overrightarrow{OP} = 2(1 - h)\mathbf{p} + h\mathbf{q}$. [1]

(c) Given also that $\overrightarrow{OP} = k\overrightarrow{OQ}$, form an equation involving **p**, **q**, h and k and use it to find the numerical values of h and k. [3]

(d) Write down the numerical value of $\dfrac{PQ}{OQ}$. [1]

(e) Given that the area of $\triangle OAB$ is 15 cm^2, calculate the area of
(i) $\triangle OBT$,
(ii) $\triangle OBP$. [2]

12. The number of patients each day in 300 days of a certain clinic are given in the following table.

No. of patients (x)	$\leqslant 25$	$25 < x \leqslant 50$	$50 < x \leqslant 75$	$75 < x \leqslant 100$	$100 < x \leqslant 125$	$125 < x \leqslant 150$
No. of days	24	33	60	118	60	5

(a) Copy and complete the following cumulative frequency table.

No. of patients (x)	$\leqslant 25$	$\leqslant 50$	$\leqslant 75$	$\leqslant 100$	$\leqslant 125$	$\leqslant 150$
No. of days	24		117			300

[1]

(b) Using a horizontal scale of 2 cm to represent 25 patients and a vertical scale of 2 cm to represent 50 days, draw a smooth cumulative frequency curve for this distribution. [3]

(c) Showing your method clearly, use your graph to estimate
(i) the number of days with 55 patients or less, [1]
(ii) the median of the distribution, [2]
(iii) the percentage of days with more than 110 patients. [2]

(d) If one of the 300 days is chosen at random, calculate the probability that it has not more than 75 patients, expressing your answer as a fraction in its simplest form. [1]

(e) If two of the 300 days are chosen at random, calculate the probability that both days have more than 125 patients each, giving your answer as a fraction in its simplest form. [2]

ASSESSMENT PAPER SET B (PAPER 1)

Time : $2\frac{1}{2}$ hours
Marks: 100

Answer *all* questions.
Write your answers in the spaces provided on the question paper.
If working is needed for any question, show it in the space below that question.
Omission of essential working will result in loss of marks.
No calculators may be used in this paper.
The number of marks is given in brackets [ ] at the end of each part question.
This paper consists of 29 questions.

1. Calculate the exact value of
(a) 0.042×0.47, [1]
(b) $0.7 \div 0.042$. [2]

Ans (a) ____________________

(b) ____________________

2. Given that $p = 4$ and $q = -3$, evaluate
(a) $4p - q^2$, [1]
(b) $2q^3$, [1]
(c) $q(1 - 3p)$. [1]

Ans (a) ____________________

(b) ____________________

(c) ____________________

3. Express

(a) 0.006 3 in standard form, [1]

(b) $\frac{13}{40}$ as a percentage, [1]

(c) 0.135 as a fraction in its lowest term. [1]

Ans (a) ____________________

(b) ____________________

(c) ____________________

4. **(a)** Find the cost of 0.85 kg of mutton costing 96¢ per 100 g. [1]

(b) There are 30 pupils in a class. A teacher gives each pupil 3 gummy sweets. A packet consisting of 12 gummy sweets costs $3.25.

(i) How many packets of gummy sweets does she need to buy? [1]

(ii) How much would it cost her? [1]

Ans (a) ____________________

(b) (i) ____________________

(ii) ____________________

5. Factorise completely

(a) $2a^3 + 18a$, [1]

(b) $3x^2 - 5x - 2$. [2]

Ans (a) ______________________

(b) ______________________

6. Giving your answer as a fraction in its lowest term, find the exact value of

(a) $1\frac{3}{5} - \frac{3}{4}$, [1]

(b) $2\frac{1}{4} \div 3 \times \frac{2}{3}$. [2]

Ans (a) ______________________

(b) ______________________

7. **(a)** Estimate, correct to 1 significant figure, the value of 44.921 458 – 26.317 221. [1]

(b) Evaluate $\dfrac{1}{0.2 + \dfrac{2}{3}}$. [2]

Ans (a) ______________________

(b) ______________________

8. Evaluate

(a) 9^{-2}, [1]

(b) $16^0 \times 16^{\frac{1}{4}}$, [1]

(c) $32^{\frac{3}{5}}$. [1]

Ans (a) ______________________

(b) ______________________

(c) ______________________

9. **(a)** Solve the inequality $5 - 2x \geqslant 7$. [1]

(b) List the integer values of y for which

$$-3 \leqslant y < 1 \text{ and } 11 + 3y < 15.$$ [2]

Ans (a) ____________________

(b) ____________________

10. In the diagram, $ABCD$ is a quadrilateral in which $A\hat{B}C = 130°$, $B\hat{C}D = 105°$, $B\hat{A}D = 80°$ and $AB = BC$. The point X on AD is such that AB is parallel to XC. Calculate

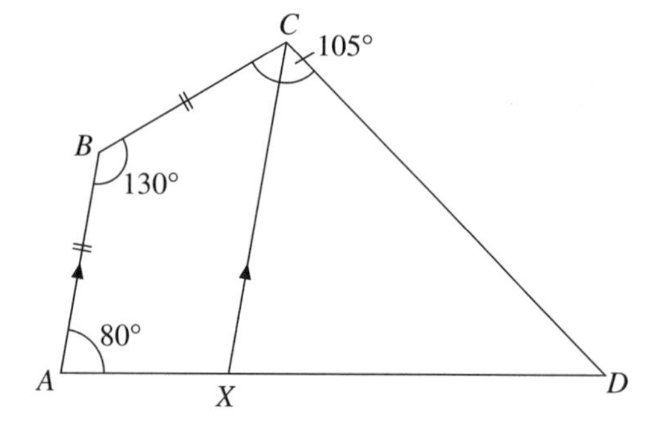

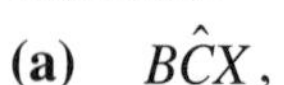

(a) $B\hat{C}X$, [1]

(b) $C\hat{D}X$, [1]

(c) $C\hat{A}X$. [1]

Ans (a) ____________________

(b) ____________________

(c) ____________________

11. Solve the simultaneous equations.

$$6x - 7y = 23$$
$$9x + 4y = -9$$

[3]

Ans ______________________

12.

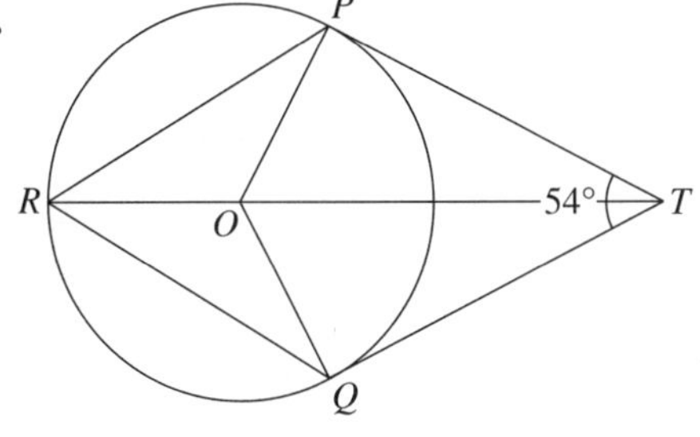

TP and TQ are tangents to a circle centre O. ROT is a straight line and $P\hat{T}Q = 54°$.

(a) Name the axis of symmetry in the diagram. [1]

(b) Calculate $R\hat{P}T$. [1]

(c) Given that P, Q, R, T and O are points on the ground, find the bearing of P from O. [1]

Ans (a) ______________________

(b) ______________________

(c) ______________________

13. $A\hat{B}C = 90°$, $AD = 13$ cm, $BC = 8$ cm and $CD = 4$ cm. Calculate

(a) AB, [1]

(b) $\cos A\hat{D}C$, [1]

(c) $\tan A\hat{C}D$. [1]

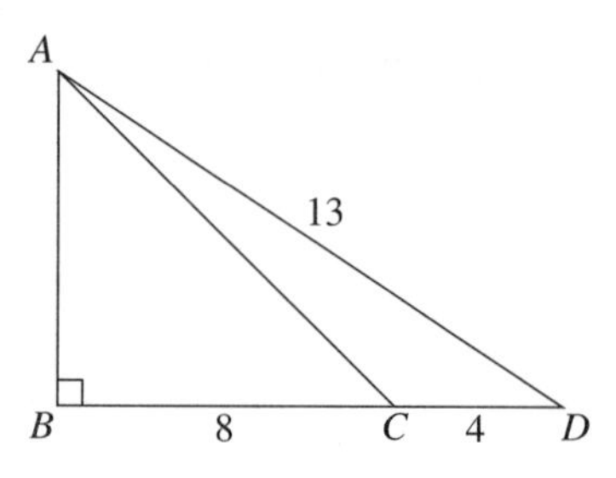

Ans (a) ______________________

(b) ______________________

(c) ______________________

14. Given that $-5 \leqslant a \leqslant 3$ and $2 \leqslant b \leqslant 7$, find

(a) the greatest possible value of $a + b$, [1]

(b) the smallest possible value of $a - b$, [1]

(c) the least possible value of ab. [1]

Ans (a) ______________________

(b) ______________________

(c) ______________________

15. Peter and Paul participated in a 4.8 km cross-country run. It took Peter 25 minutes 25 seconds and it took Paul 32 minutes 5 seconds to complete the run.

(a) Calculate, in minutes and seconds, how much longer it took Paul to complete the run. [1]

(b) Express, as simply as possible, the ratio of Peter's time to Paul's time in the form $x : y$. [2]

Ans (a) ____________________

(b) ____________________

16. Solve the equations.

(a) $7\sqrt{x} = 4$ [1]

(b) $\frac{3}{y + 2} = \frac{5}{y}$ [2]

Ans (a) ____________________

(b) ____________________

17. The points A, B, C and D lie on a circle centre O. $C\hat{O}D = 80°$ and $A\hat{B}C = 70°$. Calculate

(a) $C\hat{A}D$, [1]

(b) $A\hat{D}O$, [1]

(c) $A\hat{C}O$, [1]

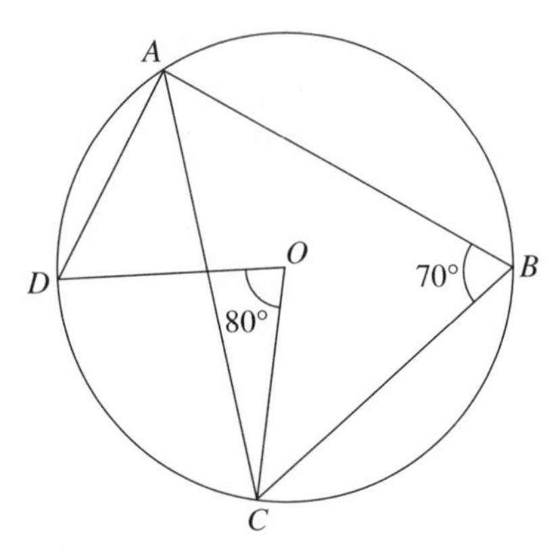

Ans (a) ____________________

(b) ____________________

(c) ____________________

18. **(a)** Mr Tan went with four friends to a restaurant for set lunch. If each set costs \$13.89, how much did their meal cost altogether? [1]

(b) Mr Tan brought his wife and three children to the zoo on Sunday. If each adult ticket costs \$12.80 and Mr Tan paid \$54.40 altogether, calculate the cost of a child's ticket. [1]

(c) Mr Tan bought a video camera priced at \$2 000, and he was given a discount of $4\frac{1}{2}\%$. Calculate the price he paid. [1]

Ans (a) ____________________

(b) ____________________

(c) ____________________

19. A class of 40 pupils were asked how many pens they had with them. The results are shown in the table.

No. of pens	0	1	2	3
No. of pupils	2	4	22	12

For this distribution, find

(a) the median, [1]

(b) the mean. [2]

Ans (a) ______________________

(b) ______________________

20. It is given that $y = \frac{kx}{z^2}$ and that $y = 3$ when $x = 9$ and $z = 6$.

(a) Calculate the value of k. [1]

(b) Hence, calculate the values of z when $y = 144$ and $x = 3$. [2]

Ans (a) ______________________

(b) ______________________

21. $\mathbf{p} = \begin{pmatrix} -8 \\ 15 \end{pmatrix}$, $\mathbf{q} = \begin{pmatrix} 9 \\ 7 \end{pmatrix}$ and $\mathbf{r} = \begin{pmatrix} k \\ 6 \end{pmatrix}$.

(a) Express $\mathbf{p} - 2\mathbf{q}$ as a column vector. [1]

(b) Find $|\mathbf{p}|$. [1]

(c) Given that $\mathbf{r}$ is parallel to $\mathbf{p}$, find the value of k. [1]

Ans (a) ____________________

(b) ____________________

(c) ____________________

22. The diagram shows the speed-time graph of an object which travels at a uniform speed of 56 m/s for 5 seconds and then slows down uniformly, coming to rest after a further 4 seconds. Calculate

(a) the speed of the object after 8 seconds, [1]

(b) the average speed of the object during the 9 seconds. [2]

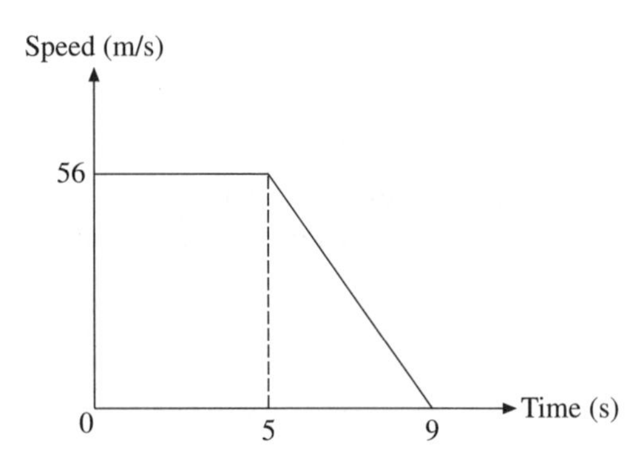

Ans (a) ____________________

(b) ____________________

23. 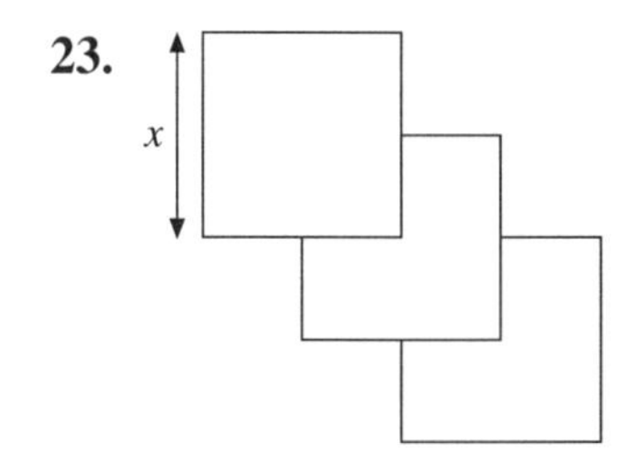

The diagram is made up of three equal squares, one overlapping the other at the midpoint of the sides. The sides of each square are of length x m.

(a) Find an expression, in terms of x, for

(i) the perimeter of the diagram, [1]

(ii) the area of the diagram. [1]

(b) Hence, or otherwise, find the value of x when

(i) the perimeter of the diagram is 25 cm, [1]

(ii) the area of the diagram is 90 cm^2. [1]

Ans (a) (i) ____________________

(ii) ____________________

(b) (i) ____________________

(ii) ____________________

24. The diagram shows three points $A(-2, 1)$, $B(4, 1)$ and $C(6, 5)$.
Calculate

(a) the gradient of the line AC, [1]

(b) the equation of the line AC, [1]

(c) the area of triangle ABC. [2]

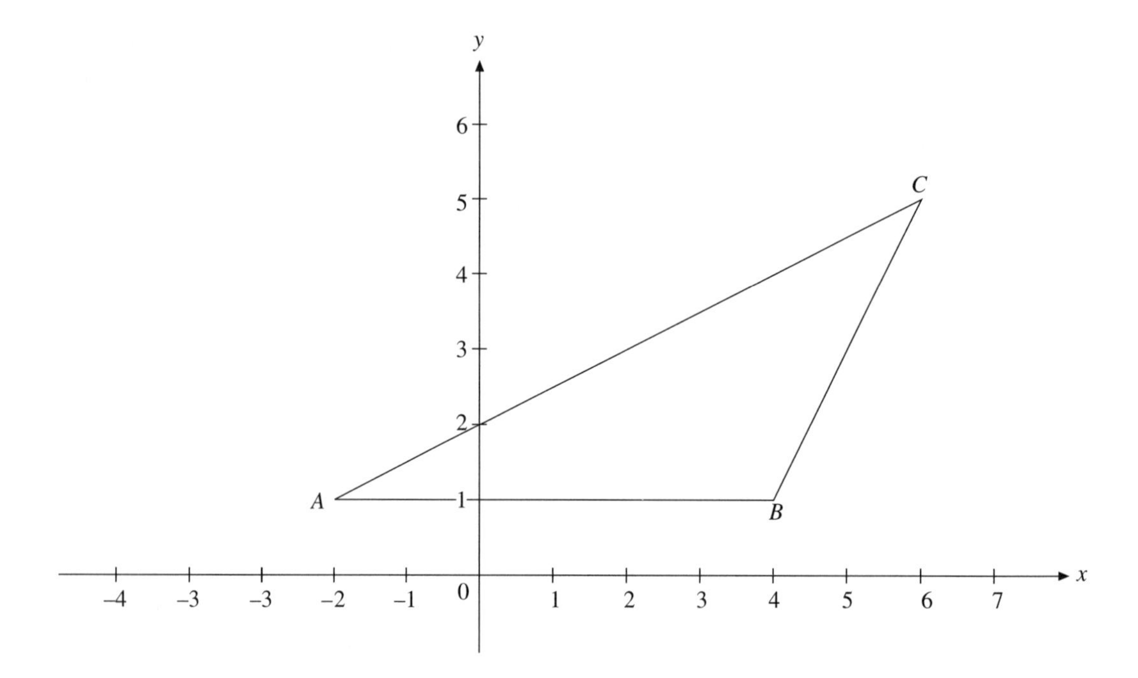

Ans (a) ____________________

(b) ____________________

(c) ____________________

25. Triangle P has vertices (1, 2), (1, 1) and (3, 1). Triangle Q has vertices (1, –4), (1, –2) and (–3, –2). Triangle R has vertices (1, 4), (1, 3) and (3, 7).

(a) Describe completely the single transformation which maps triangle P onto triangle Q. [2]

(b) Describe completely the single transformation which maps triangle P onto triangle R. [2]

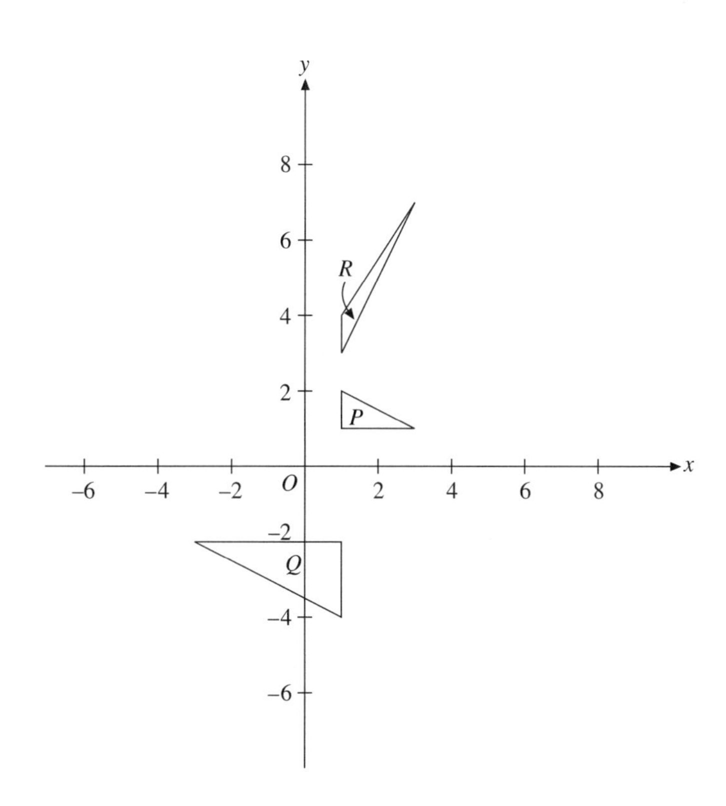

Ans (a) ______________________________

____

(b) ______________________________

____

26. In triangle ABC, $AB = 5$ cm, $AC = 8$ cm and $B\hat{A}C = 60°$. Using as much of the information given below as is necessary, calculate

(a) the area of triangle ABC, [2]

(b) BC. [3]

[$\sin 60° = 0.866$, $\cos 60° = 0.500$, $\tan 60° = 1.732$]

Ans (a) ____________________

(b) ____________________

27. The heights of two similar solid pyramids are in the ratio 4 : 5.

(a) State the ratio of the perimeter of their bases. [1]

(b) Given that the mass of the smaller pyramid is 6.4 kg, and that the density of the material from which the pyramids are made is 12.8 g/cm^3, find

(i) the mass of the larger pyramid, [2]

(ii) the volume of the smaller pyramid. [2]

Ans (a) ____________________

(b) (i) ____________________

(ii) ____________________

28. In the diagram below, draw the locus of points which are

(a) 3 cm from A, [2]

(b) equidistant from A and B, [2]

(c) 2 cm from AB. [2]

A

B

29. Two boxes contain coloured paper clips. Box A contains 8 blue paper clips, 4 yellow paper clips and 3 green paper clips. Box B contains 6 blue paper clips and 3 green paper clips.

(a) One paper clip is chosen at random from box A. Find the probability that it is not green. [1]

(b) Two paper clips are chosen at random from box B. Find the probability that they are both blue. [2]

(c) All the paper clips are replaced in their original boxes and then one paper clip is chosen from each box. Find the probability that

(i) one is yellow and one is green, [1]

(ii) one is blue and one is green. [2]

Ans (a) ____________________

(b) ____________________

(c) (i) ____________________

(ii) ____________________

ASSESSMENT PAPER SET B (PAPER 2)

Time : $2\frac{1}{2}$ **hours**
Marks: 100

This paper consists of 2 sections.
Section A consists of **5 questions**.
Section B consists of **7 questions**.
Calculators may be used in this paper. If the degree of accuracy is not specified and if the answer is not exact, the answer should be given to three significant figures.

Section A (52 marks)
ALL *questions may be attempted.*

1. Paul, Peter and Patrick each decided to buy a new car which was priced in the showroom at $75 000.
- **(a)** Paul paid for his new car in cash and was given a discount. Given that he paid $69 000 for his new car, calculate the percentage discount he received. [2]
- **(b)** Peter offered his own car in part exchange and the salesman allowed him $29 600 towards the cost of the new car. He took a loan of the balance amount from a finance company for a period of 8 years. If the finance company charges simple interest at a rate of 4.75% per annum on car financing, calculate
  - **(i)** the amount Peter borrowed, [1]
  - **(ii)** the total interest paid by Peter, [2]
  - **(iii)** the amount of each monthly instalment. [2]
- **(c)** Patrick, being the uncle of the salesman, was allowed to pay 40% of the showroom price of the car as a deposit and the balance in equal monthly instalments over a period of 2 years. Calculate the amount of each monthly instalment. [2]
- **(d)** The salesman had hoped to sell each new car for $75 000, so that he would make a profit of 20% in the cost price. Calculate the cost price of each new car. [2]

2. **(a)** Express as a single fraction $\frac{3}{2x-1} - \frac{x}{3+2x}$. [3]
- **(b)** Solve the equations.
  - **(i)** $7 = 3d - (4 - d)$ [2]
  - **(ii)** $7 = 3e(4 - e)$ [3]
- **(c)** Given that $1 - y = \frac{1+y}{x}$, express y in terms of x. [3]

3.

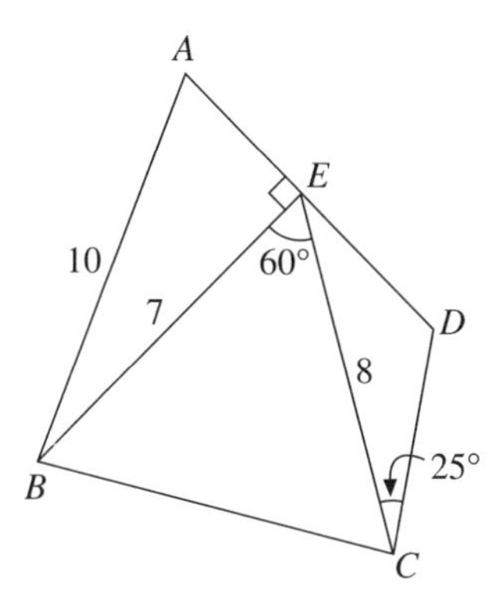

In the diagram, $AB = 10$ cm, $BE = 7$ cm, $CE = 8$ cm, $B\hat{E}C = 60°$, $A\hat{E}B = 90°$, $D\hat{C}E = 25°$ and AD is a straight line. Calculate

(a) AE, [2]

(b) $A\hat{B}E$, [2]

(c) BC, [3]

(d) $C\hat{D}E$, [1]

(e) DE. [2]

4.

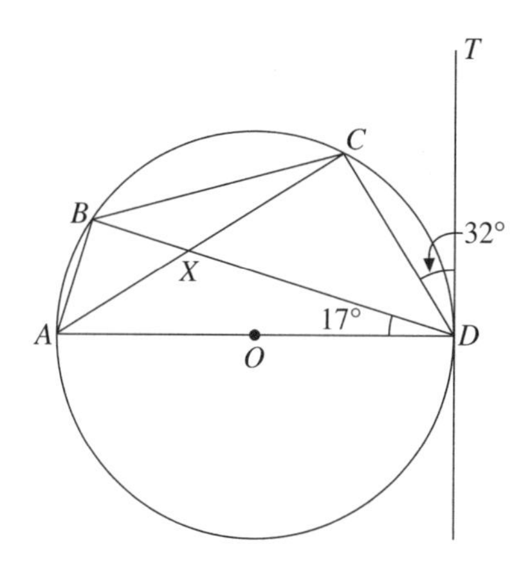

AD is a diameter of the circle, DT is the tangent at D and the diagonals, AC and BD intersect at X.

(a) Given that $C\hat{D}T = 32°$ and $A\hat{D}B = 17°$, calculate

(i) $C\hat{A}B$, [2]

(ii) $B\hat{C}D$. [2]

(b) **(i)** Prove, stating your reasons clearly, that $\triangle BCX$ and $\triangle ADX$ are similar. [2]

(ii) Given that $BC = \frac{3}{4}AD$ and $CX = 4.2$ cm, calculate the length of DX. [2]

(iii) Calculate, as a fraction, the numerical value of the ratio $\frac{\text{area of } \triangle BCX}{\text{area of } \triangle ADX}$. [2]

5. The following table shows the height of 20 pupils and their Mathematics test scores.

Pupil	Height in cm	Marks	Pupil	Height in cm	Marks
A	130	90	*K*	135	76
B	134	93	*L*	130	80
C	131	84	*M*	131	74
D	130	65	*N*	135	67
E	131	74	*O*	132	70
F	132	78	*P*	132	85
G	134	58	*Q*	134	98
H	133	74	*R*	135	74
I	130	69	*S*	132	63
J	132	92	*T*	132	76

(a) Construct a dot diagram for the height of pupils. [2]
(b) Write down the height that has the greatest frequency. [1]
(c) Make a stem-and-leaf plot for the Mathematics test scores. [2]
(d) What is the lowest score? What is the highest score? [2]
(e) What score occurs most often? [1]
(f) Observe whether there is any cluster or gap present. [2]

Section B (48 marks)
Answer **four** questions in this section.
Each question in this section carries 12 marks.

6. (a)

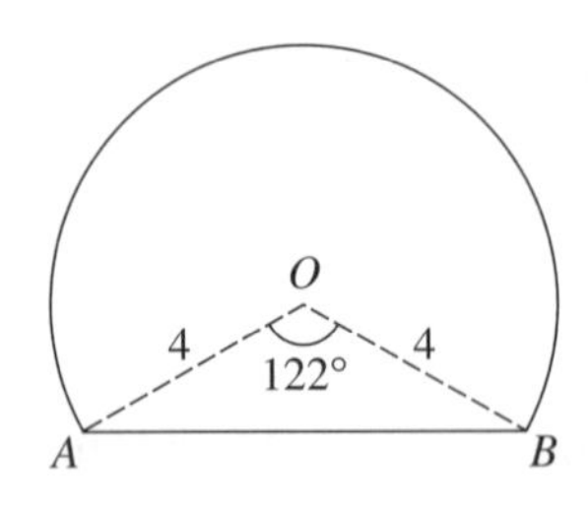

The diagram is the major segment of a circle, centre O. Given that $A\hat{O}B = 122°$, $OA = OB = 4$ cm and taking π to be 3.142, calculate

(i) the length of the chord AB, [2]
(ii) the perimeter of the segment. [3]

(b) The figure shows a solid which is made up of a cone joined to a hemisphere radius 3 cm.

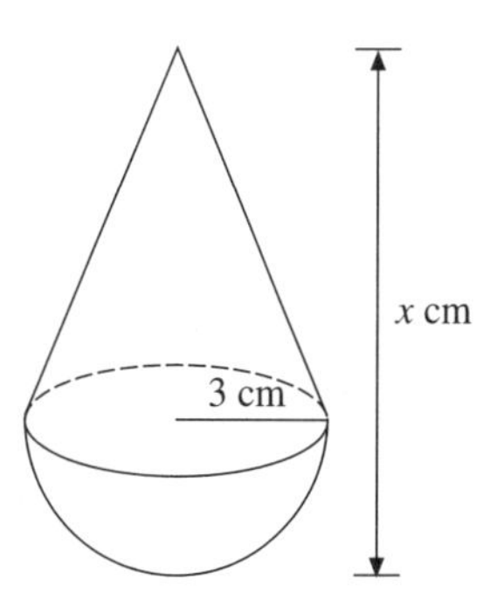

(i) Given that the volume of the solid is 39π cm^3, find

(1) the volume of the hemisphere, leaving your answer in terms of π, [1]

(2) x, the height of the solid. [2]

(ii) The solid is placed into a cylinder containing 161π cm^3 of water. Given that the water level rises up to a height of 18 cm, find the base radius of the cylinder. [4]

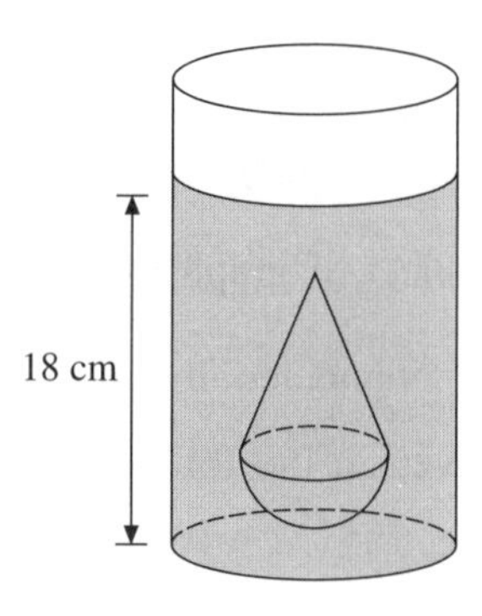

7. (a) Angela could type at an average rate of 15 pages per hour, while Brenda could type at an average rate of x pages per hour. If Angela and Brenda managed to type 8 pages altogether in 15 minutes, find x. [2]

(b) (i) Cindy typed 42 pages at an average speed of x pages per hour. Write down, in terms of x, an expression for the number of hours it took her to type the 42 pages. [1]

(ii) Dorothy typed at an average speed which was 2 pages per hour faster than Cindy's speed. Write down, in terms of x, an expression for the number of hours which Dorothy took to type the 42 pages. [1]

(iii) Given that the difference between the two times was 20 minutes, write an equation in x and show that it reduces to

$$x^2 + 2x - 252 = 0.$$ [4]

(iv) Solve the equation $x^2 + 2x - 252 = 0$, giving each of your answers correct to 1 decimal place. Hence, find the time it took Cindy to type the 42 pages. Give your answer in hours and minutes. [4]

8. The triangle ABC has vertices $A(1, 1)$, $B(2, 2)$ and $C(0, 3)$. The triangle $A_1B_1C_1$ has vertices $A_1(-2, 2)$, $B_1(-3, 3)$ and $C_1(-4, 1)$.

(a) Using a scale of 2 cm to 1 unit on each axis, draw x and y axes for $-4 \leqslant x \leqslant 5$ and $-3 \leqslant y \leqslant 9$.
Draw the triangles ABC and $A_1B_1C_1$, labelling the vertices clearly. [3]

(b) $\triangle ABC$ can be mapped onto $\triangle A_1B_1C_1$ by an anticlockwise rotation about the origin followed by a translation.

(i) State the angle of rotation. [1]

(ii) Express the translation as a column vector. [2]

(iii) Given that $\triangle ABC$ can be mapped onto $\triangle A_1B_1C_1$ by a single rotation, find the coordinates of the centre of this rotation. [2]

(c) M_1 is a reflection in the x-axis and M_2 is a reflection in the line $x = -1$.

(i) Draw and label $\triangle A_2B_2C_2$, the image of $\triangle ABC$ under M_2M_1. [2]

(ii) Describe completely the single transformation which is equivalent to M_2M_1. [2]

9. Answer this question on a sheet of graph paper.

The variables x and y are connected by the equation $y = x - \frac{x^2}{3}$ and some corresponding values are given in the following table.

x	-1	$-\frac{1}{2}$	0	1	2	3	4	4.5
y	-1.3	-0.6	0	0.7	0.7	0	-1.3	a

(a) Calculate the value of a. [1]

(b) Taking 2 cm to represent 1 unit on each axis, draw the graph of $y = x - \frac{x^2}{3}$ for values of x in the range $-1 \leqslant x \leqslant 4.5$. [4]

(c) Find, from your graph, the solutions of the equation $3x - x^2 = 1.5$. [3]

(d) **(i)** On the same axes, draw the graph of the straight line $y = \frac{x}{3} - 1$.

(ii) Use your graphs to solve the equation

$$x - \frac{x^2}{3} = \frac{x}{3} - 1.$$

(iii) Write down, but do not simplify, an equation in x which has these values as two of its solutions. [4]

10.

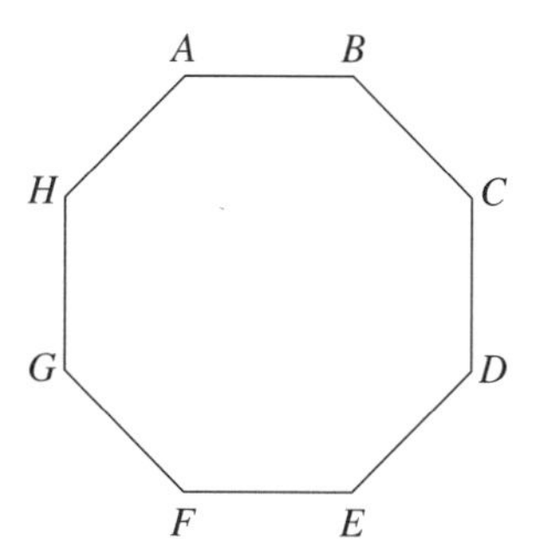

(a) *ABCDEFGH* is a regular octagon.

(i) Calculate the size of each interior angle of the octagon. [2]

(ii) Calculate $D\hat{H}E$. [3]

(b) **(i)** Construct the triangle *PQR* in which $PQ = 7.5$ cm, $QR = 6$ cm and $P\hat{Q}R = 125°$. Measure and write down the length of *PR*. [2]

(ii) On the same diagram, construct the locus of

(1) the point *X* which is such that *X* is always equidistant from the fixed points *R* and *Q*, [1]

(2) the point *Y* which is such that it is always equidistant from the lines *PQ* and *QR*, [1]

(3) the point *Z* which is such that it is always on the same side of *PQ* as *R* and $P\hat{Z}Q$ is always 90°. [1]

(iii) The point *W* inside triangle *PQR* is such that it satisfies all the following conditions:

(1) It is on the same side of *PQ* as *R*.

(2) It is nearer to the line *QR* than the line *PQ*.

(3) $WQ \leqslant WR$

(4) $P\hat{W}Q \leqslant 90°$

Indicate clearly, by shading, the region in which *W* must lie. [2]

11. The cumulative distribution of marks scored by 400 candidates in an examination is given in the table below.

Mark	10	20	30	40	50	60	70	80	90	100
No. of candidates scoring this mark or less	5	20	47	95	160	245	325	368	390	400

(a) Calculate how many candidates scored a mark between 61 and 70 inclusive. [1]

(b) Using a horizontal scale of 2 cm to represent 20 marks and a vertical scale of 2 cm to represent 50 candidates, draw a cumulative frequency curve to illustrate the information. [3]

(c) Showing your method clearly, use your graph to estimate

(i) the median mark, [1]

(ii) the interquartile range, [1]

(iii) the percentage of candidates who passed the examination, if the pass mark is 45. [2]

(d) **(i)** Use your graph to estimate the number of candidates whose marks lie between 45 and 55. [1]

(ii) Find the probability that a candidate chosen at random will have a mark that does not lie between 45 and 55. [1]

(e) Two candidates are chosen at random. Find the probability that one has a mark less than or equal to 40 and the other has a mark greater than 80. [2]

12.

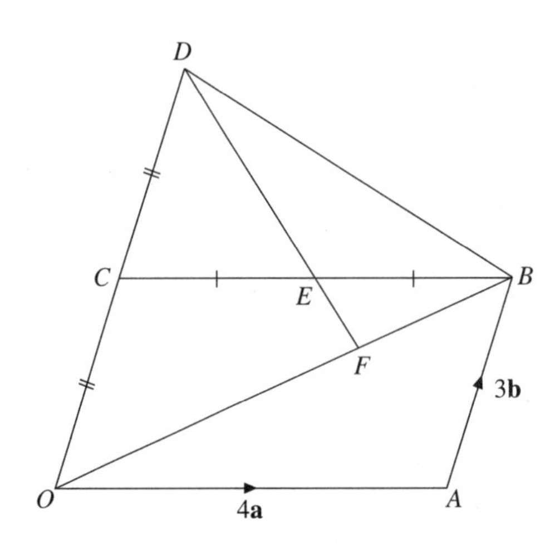

OABC is a parallelogram and *E* is the midpoint of *BC*. *OC* is produced to *D* so that $OC = CD$. *DE* is produced to meet *OB* at *F*.

(a) Given that $\overrightarrow{OA} = 4\mathbf{a}$ and $\overrightarrow{AB} = 3\mathbf{b}$, express, in terms of **a** and/or **b**,

(i) $\overrightarrow{OB}$,

(ii) $\overrightarrow{BD}$,

(iii) $\overrightarrow{DE}$. [3]

(b) Given that $\overrightarrow{DF} = h\overrightarrow{DE}$, express $\overrightarrow{DF}$ in terms of **a**, **b** and h. [1]

(c) Hence show that $\overrightarrow{FB} = 2(2 - h)\mathbf{a} + 3(h - 1)\mathbf{b}$. [2]

(d) Given also that $\overrightarrow{FB} = k\overrightarrow{OB}$, express $\overrightarrow{FB}$ in terms of **a**, **b** and k. [1]

(e) Using these two expressions for $\overrightarrow{FB}$, find the value of h and the value of k. [2]

(f) Find the ratio $OF : FB$. [2]

(g) Find the numerical value of $\dfrac{\text{area of } \triangle OBD}{\text{area of trapezium } OABD}$. [1]

ANSWERS

Chapter 1

1. (a)

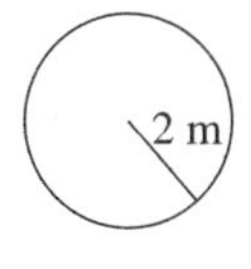

A circle of radius 2 m
Area = 4π m^2

(b)

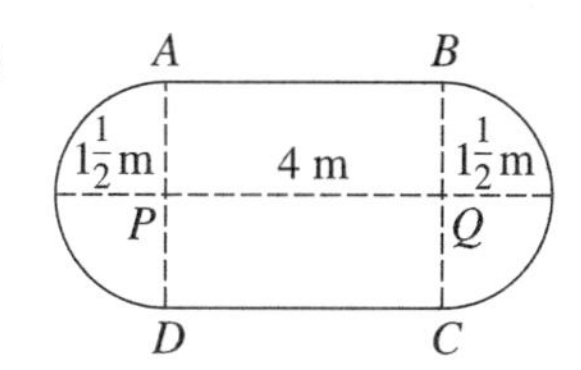

The locus is made up of a rectangle $ABCD$, 4 m by 3 m, and two semicircles of radius $1\frac{1}{2}$ m with centres P and Q as shown above.
Area = 19.1 m^2

(c)

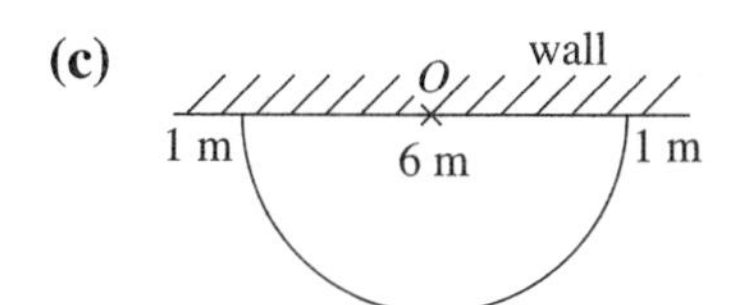

A semicircle of radius 3 m with centre O
Area = $\frac{9}{2}\pi$ m^2

(d) (i)

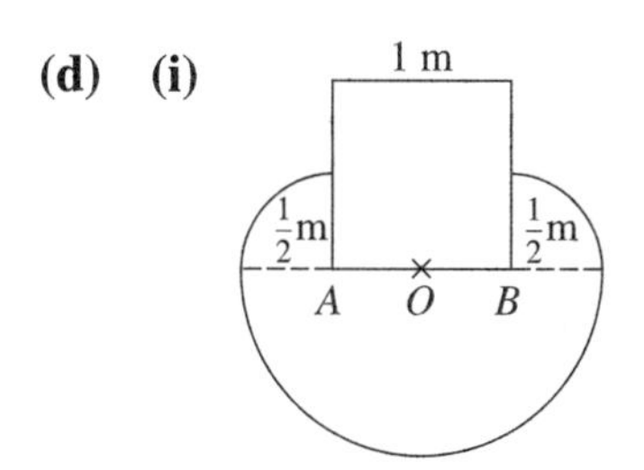

The locus is made up of a semicircle of radius 1 m and two quadrants of radius $\frac{1}{2}$ m with centres O, A and B as shown.
Area = $\frac{1}{2}\pi$ m^2

(ii)

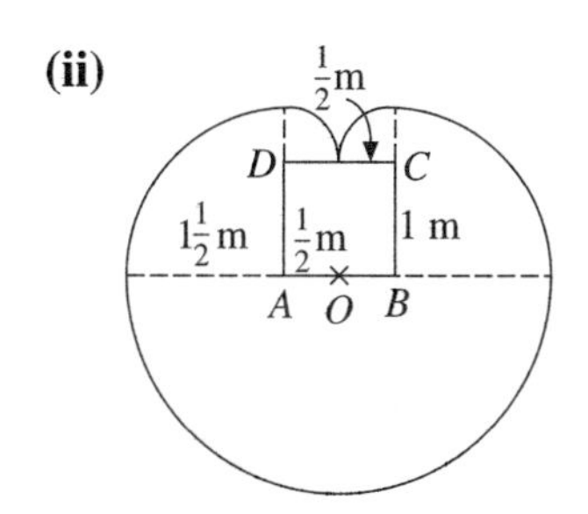

The locus is made up of a semicircle of radius 2 m, two quadrants of radius $1\frac{1}{2}$ m and two quadrants of radius $\frac{1}{2}$ m with centres O, A, B, C and D respectively.
Area = $\frac{13}{4}\pi$ m^2

(e) (i)

2 m A
1 m
B
1 m

The locus is made up of a quadrant of radius 2 m and a quadrant of radius 1 m with centres A and B as shown.
Area = $\frac{5}{4}\pi$ m^2

(ii)

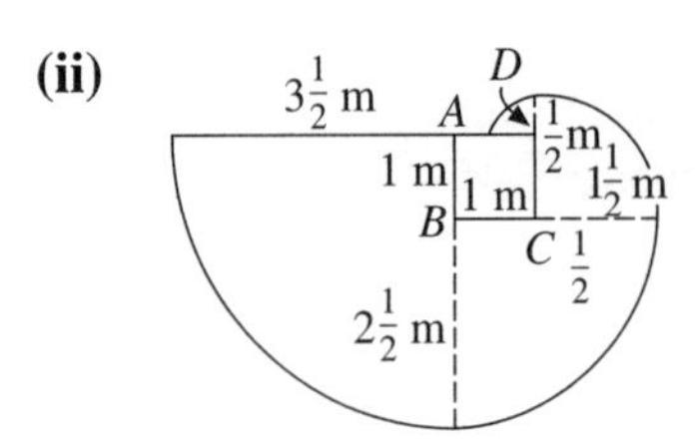

The locus consists of four quadrants of radius $3\frac{1}{2}$ m, $2\frac{1}{2}$ m, $1\frac{1}{2}$ m and $\frac{1}{2}$ m with centres A, B, C and D respectively as shown.

Area = $\frac{21}{4}\pi$ m^2

2. (a)

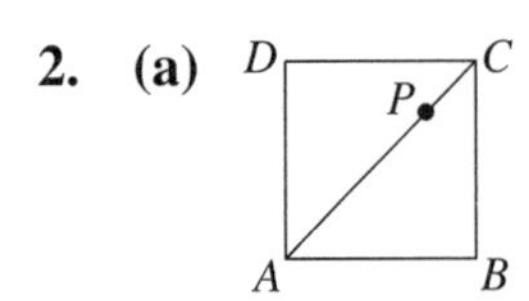

The diagonal AC

(b)

The triangle ABC

3. (a)

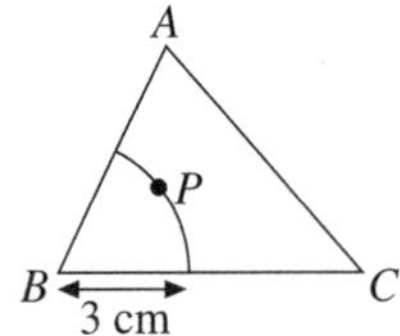

The arc of a circle of radius 3 cm and centre at B

(b)

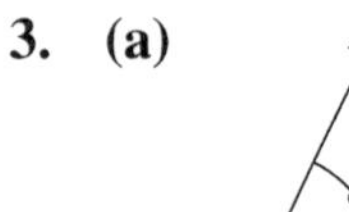

The sector of a circle of radius 3 cm and centre at B

4. (a)

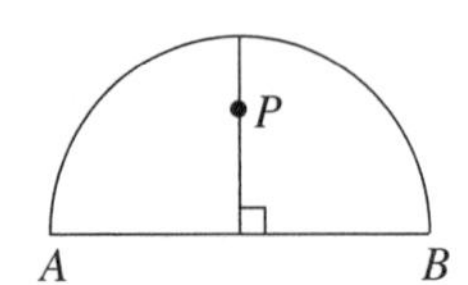

The perpendicular bisector of AB

(b)

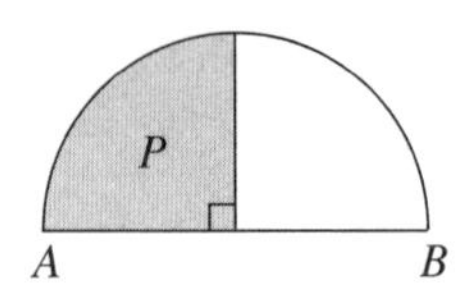

A quadrant

5.

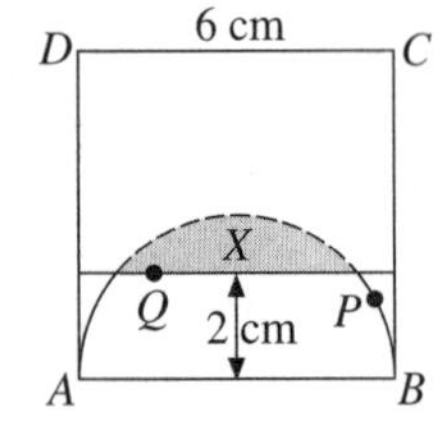

(a) **(i)** A semicircle of diameter AB

(ii) A line parallel to AB and 2 cm from it

6.

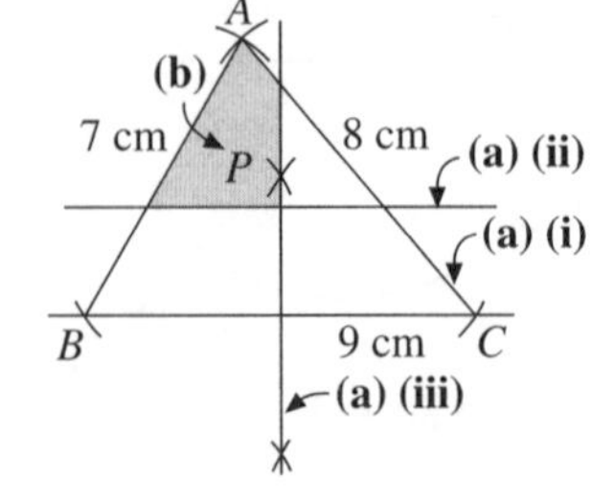

7.

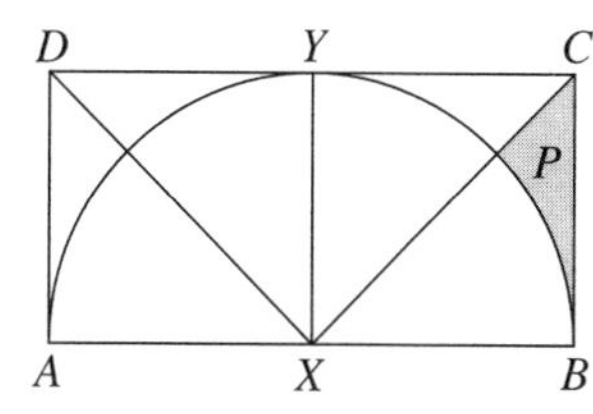

8.

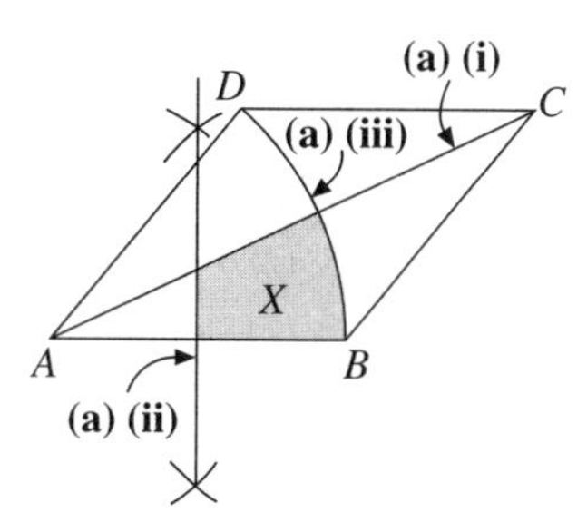

9.

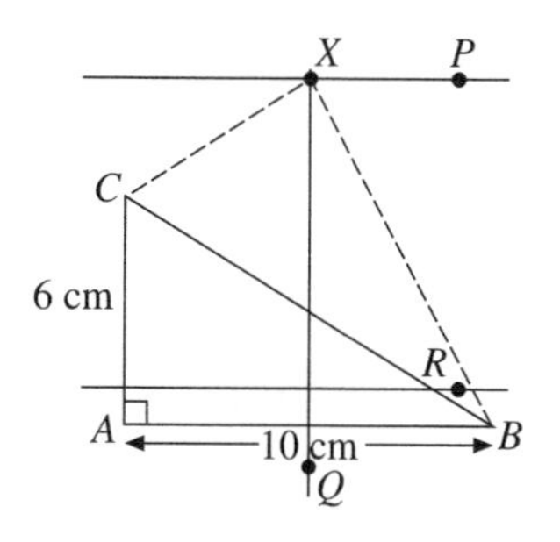

(a) 30 cm^2
(c) 60 cm^2

10.

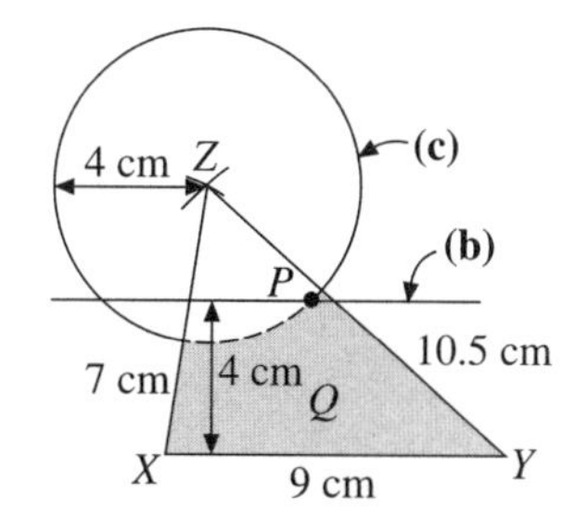

(d) 5.5 cm

11.

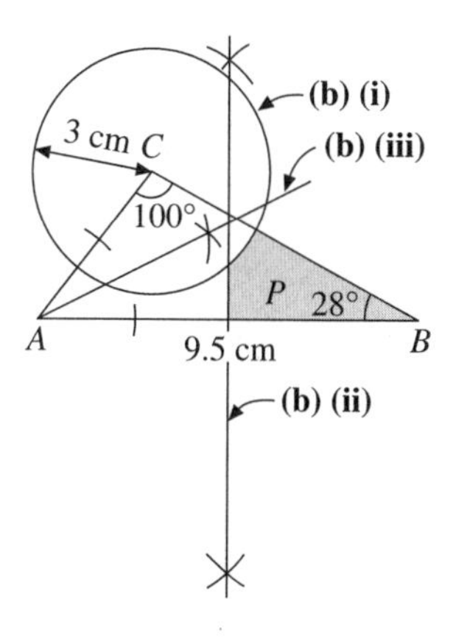

(a) 7.6 cm

12.

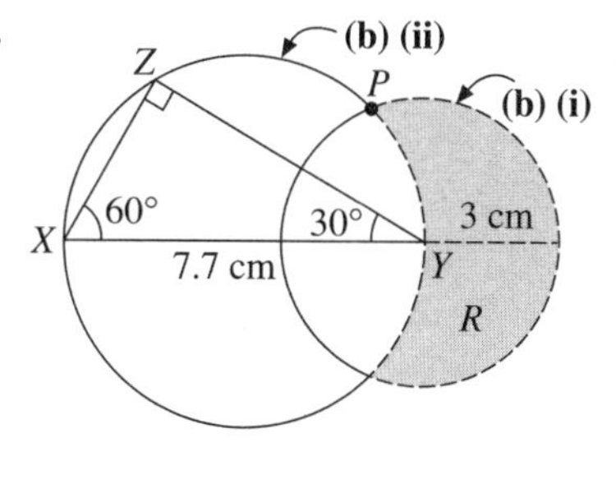

13.

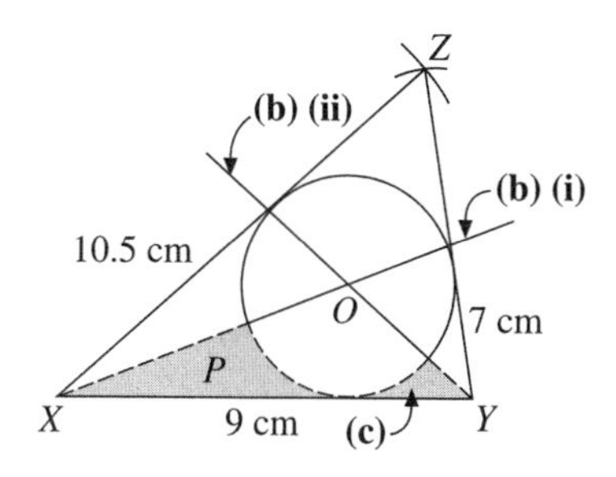

(a) 80°
(c) 2.35 cm

14.

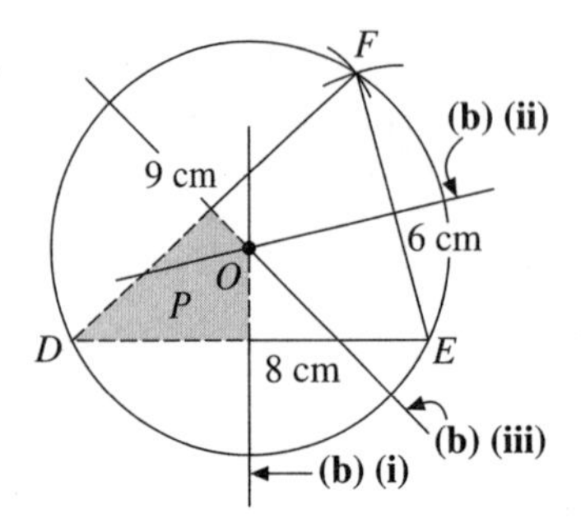

(a) 62°
(b) **(iv)** 4.6 cm

15.

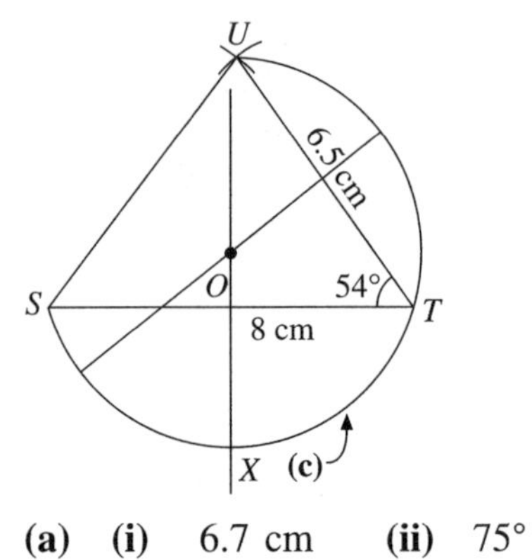

(a) **(i)** 6.7 cm **(ii)** 75°
(b) **(ii)** 4.2 cm

16.

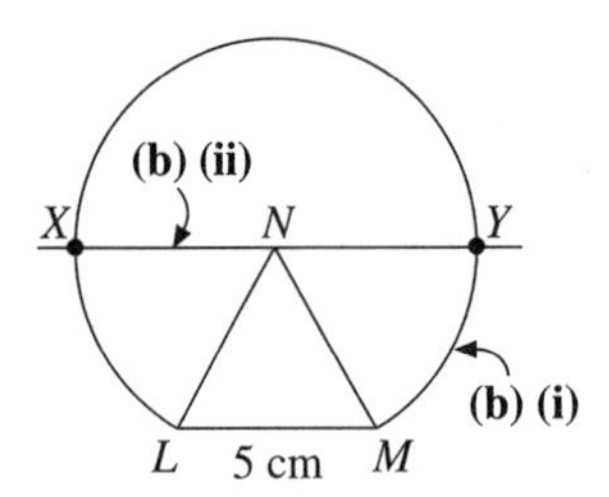

17.

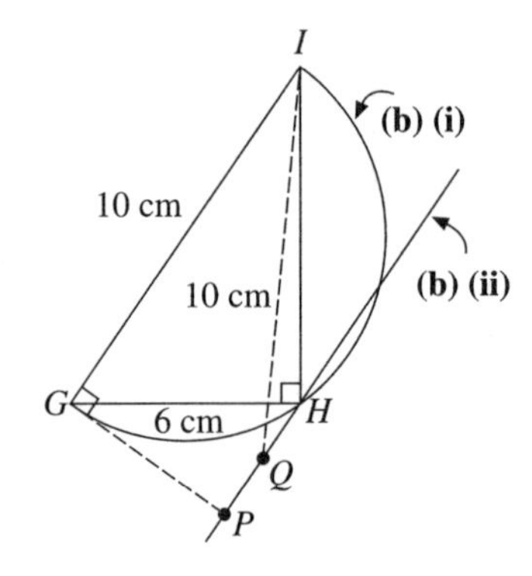

(a) **(i)** 8 cm **(ii)** 53°

18.

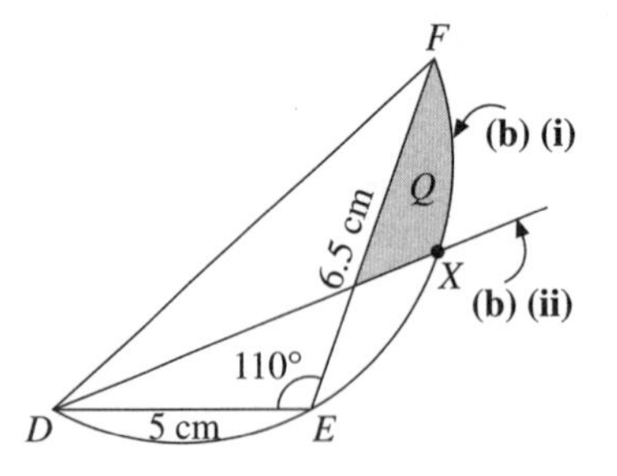

19.

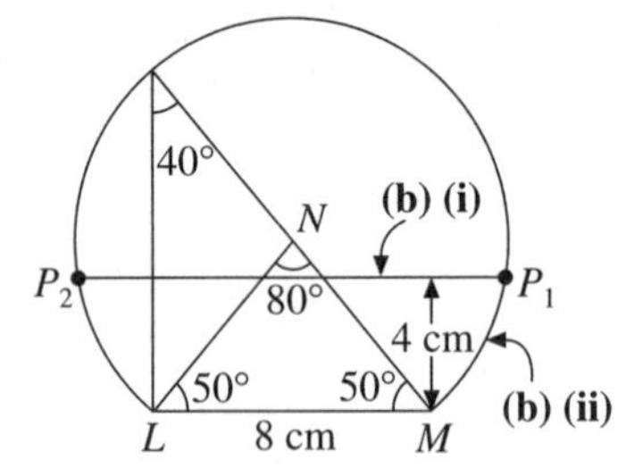

20.

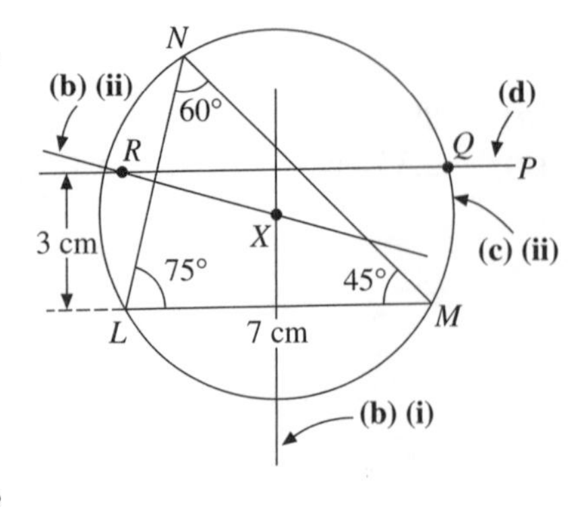

(a) 60°
(c) **(i)** 4 cm

21.

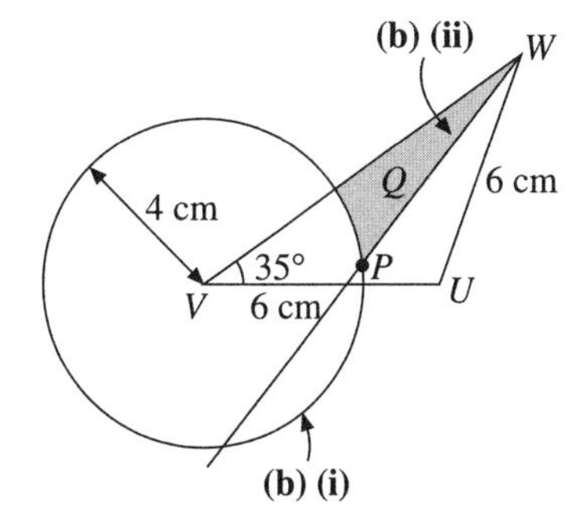

(c) (ii) 2.1 cm

22.

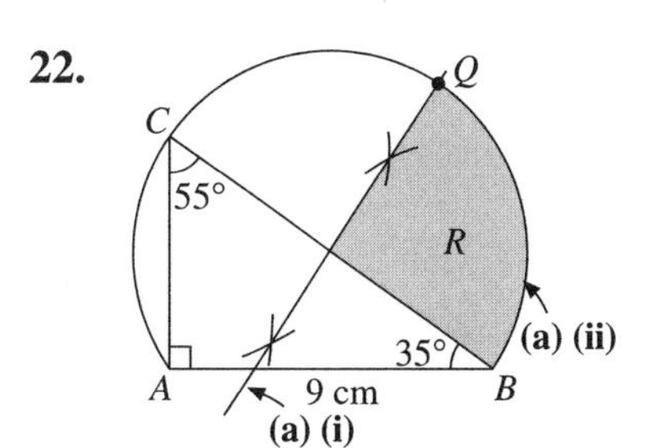

(b) (ii) 7.8 cm

23.

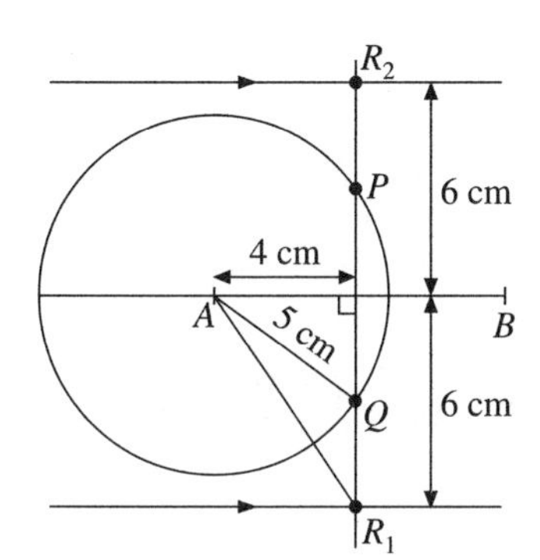

(a) **(i)** A circle of radius 5 cm and centre at *A*
(ii) Perpendicular bisector of *AB*
(iii) A pair of lines parallel to *AB* and 6 cm from it
(b) **(ii)** 6 cm
(c) 7.21 cm

24. **(a)** The locus is a pair of parallel lines with *l* as the axis.
(b) The locus is a circle with centre *O* and radius 6 cm.
(c) The locus is a line which bisects *AB* perpendicularly.

Chapter 2

1. $\mathbf{a} = -\mathbf{r}$, $\mathbf{b} = 2\mathbf{r}$, $\mathbf{c} = -\frac{1}{2}\mathbf{r}$

3. **(a)** $\overrightarrow{AC}$ **(b)** $\overrightarrow{AD}$ **(c)** $\overrightarrow{DB}$ **(d)** $\overrightarrow{BC}$

4. **(b)** They lie on a straight line. **(c)** They are parallel.
(d) **(i)** They are collinear. **(ii)** They are parallel.

5. $\overrightarrow{CA} = -(\mathbf{a} + \mathbf{b})$, $\overrightarrow{DC} = \frac{1}{2}\mathbf{a} + \mathbf{b}$

6. **(a)** $\overrightarrow{AB} = \mathbf{b} - 2\mathbf{a}$, $\overrightarrow{BC} = 2(\mathbf{b} - 2\mathbf{a})$
(b) $\overrightarrow{AB}$ and $\overrightarrow{BC}$ are parallel. Since *B* is a common point, therefore, *A*, *B* and *C* lie on a straight line.

7. **(a)** $-\mathbf{a}$ **(b)** $\mathbf{a} + \mathbf{b}$ **(c)** $-\mathbf{a}$
(d) $\mathbf{a}$ **(e)** $\mathbf{b} - \mathbf{a}$ **(f)** $2\mathbf{b} - 2\mathbf{a}$

9. $\overrightarrow{AP} = -\frac{1}{4}\mathbf{a}$, $\overrightarrow{AQ} = \frac{3}{5}(\mathbf{b} - \mathbf{a})$, $\overrightarrow{PQ} = \frac{1}{20}(12\mathbf{b} - 7\mathbf{a})$

10. **(a)** $\begin{pmatrix} 7 \\ -9 \end{pmatrix}$ **(b)** $\begin{pmatrix} 1 \\ 8 \end{pmatrix}$ **(c)** $\begin{pmatrix} -1 \\ -1\frac{3}{4} \end{pmatrix}$

11. **(a)** $3\sqrt{2}$ **(b)** 13 **(c)** 15

12. **(a)** $\sqrt{65}$ **(b)** $\begin{pmatrix} 1\frac{1}{2} \\ 1 \end{pmatrix}$

13. $h = 3$, $k = -2$

14. **(a)** $\overrightarrow{PQ} = \begin{pmatrix} 1 \\ -1 \end{pmatrix}$, $\overrightarrow{RS} = \begin{pmatrix} 2 \\ -2 \end{pmatrix}$ **(b)** They are parallel.

15. **(a)** $\begin{pmatrix} 3 \\ 12 \end{pmatrix}$ **(b)** $\begin{pmatrix} 1 \\ k - 5 \end{pmatrix}$ **(c)** $k = 9$

16. **(a)** $\sqrt{73}$ **(b)** $\left(9\frac{1}{2}, 9\right)$ **(c)** $\overrightarrow{OR} = \frac{1}{3}(\mathbf{p} + 2\mathbf{q})$

17. **(a)** 10 **(b)** $\begin{pmatrix} -3 \\ 26 \end{pmatrix}$ **(c)** $p = -5$, $q = -4\frac{1}{3}$

18. **(a)** $2\sqrt{13}$ **(b)** (9, 1) **(c)** $k = -6$

19. **(a)** $\sqrt{97}$ **(b)** $\begin{pmatrix} 7\frac{1}{2} \\ -8 \end{pmatrix}$

20. **(a)** $\begin{pmatrix} -16 \\ 15 \end{pmatrix}$ **(b)** $\begin{pmatrix} 4 \\ -6 \end{pmatrix}$

21. **(a)** $\begin{pmatrix} 0 \\ 1 \end{pmatrix}$ **(b)** 208 **(c)** $p = -\frac{3}{2}q$

22. **(a)** 25 **(b)** $\begin{pmatrix} -8 \\ 6 \end{pmatrix}$ **(c)** (29, –4) **(d)** (7, –6)

23. **(a)** $s = -16$, $t = 9$ **(b)** $\begin{pmatrix} 64 \\ -36 \end{pmatrix}$ **(c)** (58, 28)

24. $u = 6$, $v = 1$, $w = -3$, $x = -7$

25. **(a)** **(i)** $\begin{pmatrix} 7 \\ 2 \end{pmatrix}$ **(ii)** $\begin{pmatrix} 3 \\ -1 \end{pmatrix}$ **(b)** (–4, –3)

26. **(a)** 24.5 **(b)** **(i)** $\begin{pmatrix} 3 \\ 7 \end{pmatrix}$ **(ii)** $\begin{pmatrix} 1 \\ 8\frac{1}{2} \end{pmatrix}$

27. **(a)** 13 **(b)** ±12 **(c)** (5, 1) and (5, 25)

28. **(a)** $\begin{pmatrix} 4 \\ 3\frac{1}{3} \end{pmatrix}$ **(b)** $\begin{pmatrix} 2 \\ 4\frac{2}{3} \end{pmatrix}$

29. **(a)** $\begin{pmatrix} -1 \\ 2 \end{pmatrix}$ **(b)** $\begin{pmatrix} h \\ 2h \end{pmatrix}$ **(c)** $\begin{pmatrix} 2 \\ -1 \end{pmatrix}$ **(d)** $h = -\frac{1}{2}$, $k = \frac{4}{5}$

30. **(a)** $\mathbf{c} - \mathbf{b}$ **(b)** $\frac{1}{4}(\mathbf{c} - \mathbf{b})$ **(c)** $\frac{1}{2}\mathbf{b} - \mathbf{c}$ **(d)** $\frac{1}{2}(\mathbf{c} - \mathbf{b})$

(e) $\frac{1}{2}(\mathbf{b} + \mathbf{c})$ **(f)** $\frac{1}{4}(3\mathbf{b} - \mathbf{c})$ **(g)** $\frac{1}{2}\mathbf{c}$

31. **(a)** **(i)** $10\mathbf{b} - 5\mathbf{a}$ **(ii)** $4\mathbf{b} - 2\mathbf{a}$ **(iii)** $3\mathbf{a} + 4\mathbf{b}$

(b) $h = \frac{2}{3}, k = \frac{3}{5}$

32. **(a)** **(i)** $\mathbf{a} + 2\mathbf{b}$ **(ii)** $-\mathbf{b}$ **(b)** $h = 2, k = 4$

(c) P is the midpoint of OB. **(d)** $\frac{1}{3}$

33. **(a)** $\overrightarrow{QR} = \frac{1}{3}\mathbf{p} - \mathbf{q}$, $\overrightarrow{OS} = \frac{1}{4}(3\mathbf{p} + \mathbf{q})$ **(b)** $\overrightarrow{QT}$

(c) $\mathbf{q} + m(\frac{1}{3}\mathbf{p} - \mathbf{q}) = \frac{n}{4}(3\mathbf{p} + \mathbf{q})$, $m = \frac{9}{10}$, $n = \frac{2}{5}$

(d) $\overrightarrow{QT} = \frac{1}{10}(3\mathbf{p} - 9\mathbf{q})$, $\overrightarrow{OT} = \frac{1}{10}(3\mathbf{p} + \mathbf{q})$

34. **(a)** $\overrightarrow{BC} = 6\mathbf{p} - \frac{8}{3}\mathbf{q}$ **(b)** $\overrightarrow{AX} = \frac{3}{2}\overrightarrow{BC}$, $\therefore \overrightarrow{AX} \,//\, \overrightarrow{BC}$

(c) $\overrightarrow{AD} = \frac{2}{3}\mathbf{q} + k\mathbf{p}$ **(d)** $h = \frac{2}{3}, k = 4$

(e) $\overrightarrow{BD} = 4\mathbf{p} - 3\mathbf{q}$, $\overrightarrow{AD} = \frac{2}{3}(6\mathbf{p} + \mathbf{q})$

35. **(a)** **(i)** $\frac{2}{3}\mathbf{a}$ **(ii)** $\frac{3}{4}\mathbf{b}$

Test Paper 1

1.

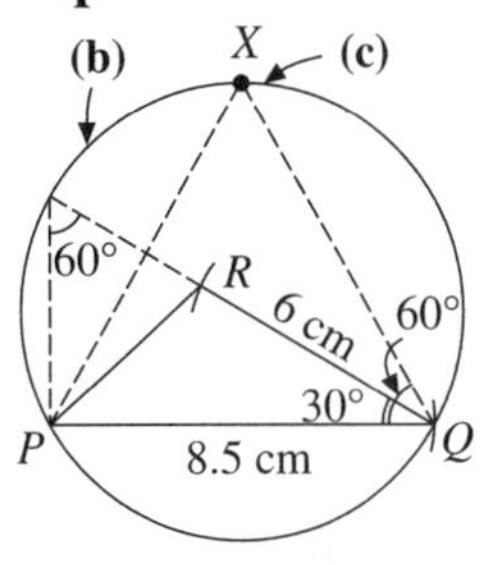

(a) 4.4 cm

2. **(a)**

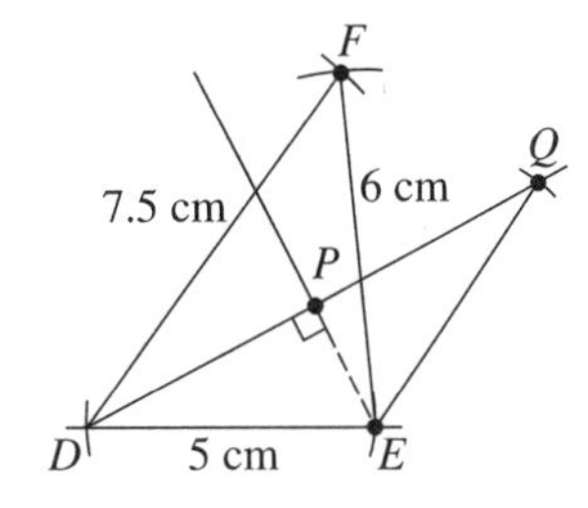

(b) **(i)** 2.25 cm  **(ii)** 126°

3.

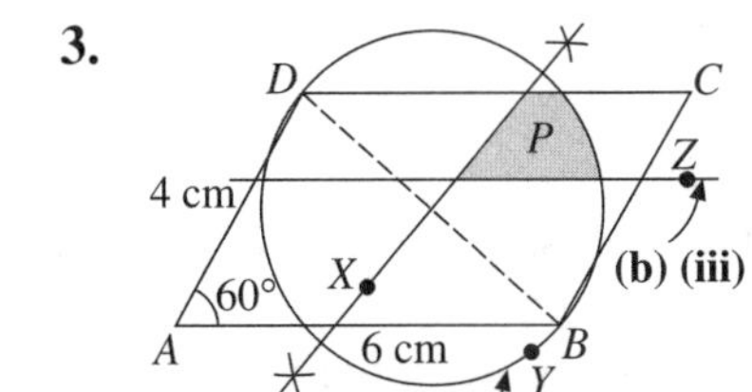

4. **(a)** The locus is a circle with centre X and radius 6 cm.
(b) The locus is a circle with centre Y and radius 2 cm.
(c) The locus is a line perpendicular to and bisecting XY.
(d) **(i)** No intersection **(ii)** A circle

5. **(a)** $\overrightarrow{DE}$ **(b)** $\overrightarrow{EB}$ **(c)** $\overrightarrow{BD}$ **(d)** $\overrightarrow{BA}$

6. **(a)** $-\frac{1}{2}\mathbf{a}$ **(b)** $\frac{5}{7}\mathbf{b}$ **(c)** $-\frac{1}{2}\mathbf{a} + \frac{2}{7}\mathbf{b}$ **(d)** $\mathbf{a} + \frac{5}{7}\mathbf{b}$

7. **(a)** **(i)** $\begin{pmatrix} 4 \\ -3 \end{pmatrix}$ **(ii)** 5 **(b)** $h = 8$

8. **(a)** $\begin{pmatrix} 11 \\ 28 \end{pmatrix}$ **(b)** $\left(-\frac{3}{4}, 9\right)$

9. **(a)** $\mathbf{c} = \frac{1}{4}(5\mathbf{a} - \mathbf{b})$ **(b)** $\mathbf{c} = \frac{1}{5}(3\mathbf{a} + 2\mathbf{b})$

10. **(a)** **(i)** $\overrightarrow{OQ} = \frac{1}{4}(\mathbf{a} + \mathbf{b})$

    (ii) $\overrightarrow{AQ} = \frac{1}{4}\mathbf{b} - \frac{3}{4}\mathbf{a}$ or $\frac{1}{4}(-3\mathbf{a} + \mathbf{b})$

    (b) $\frac{h}{4}(-3\mathbf{a} + \mathbf{b}) + \mathbf{a} = k\mathbf{b}$, $h = \frac{4}{3}$, $k = \frac{1}{3}$ **(c)** $\frac{1}{2}$

Chapter 3

1. **(a)** (3, 2) **(b)** (2, –3) **(c)** (3, –6) **(d)** (2, 3)
   (e) (0, 2) **(f)** $(4\frac{1}{2}, -3)$ **(g)** (3, –14) **(h)** (1, –2)
2. **(a)** (–7, 4) **(b)** (4, 7) **(c)** (–3, 4) **(d)** (–7, –4)
   (e) (5, –1) **(f)** $(-3\frac{1}{2}, -2)$ **(g)** (–5, 4) **(h)** (7, 2)
3. **(a)** Reflection in the line $y = x$
   (b) Reflection in the x-axis
   (c) Rotation through 90° anticlockwise
   (d) Shear parallel to the x-axis with factor 6, or stretch with factor 6 and y-axis as the invariant line
   (e) Enlargement with centre (0, 0) and factor 2
4. **(a)** $\begin{pmatrix} 5 \\ -6 \end{pmatrix}$ **(b)** **(i)** (–2, –6) **(ii)** (13, 3) **(iii)** $y = x - 15$
   (c) **(i)** (0, 0) **(ii)** (–4, 6) **(iii)** $y = 2x + 19$
5. **(a)** **(i)** (7, 2) **(ii)** (–13, –2)
   (b) **(i)** $y = -7x + 2$ **(ii)** $y = -7x - 44$
   (c) **(i)** $y = x - 5$ **(ii)** $y = x + 11$
6. **(a)** The transformation U is a shear parallel to the x-axis, with the x-axis as the invariant line and shear factor 3.
   The transformation V is a stretch parallel to the x-axis, with the y-axis as the invariant line and factor 2.
   (b) (5, –1) **(c)** (5, 6)
7. **(a)** Shear parallel to the x-axis and factor 1
   (b) Stretch parallel to the x-axis and factor 2
   (c) Reflection in the line $x = 2$
   (d) Translation $\begin{pmatrix} 2 \\ 0 \end{pmatrix}$
   (e) Clockwise rotation of 90° about (2, 0)
   (f) Rotation of 180° about (2, 1)

8.

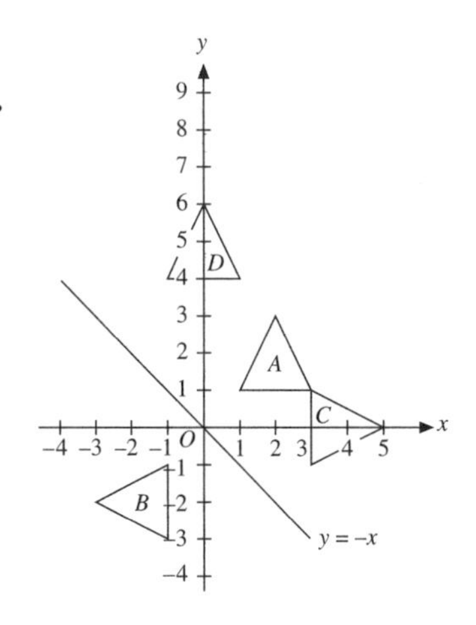

9. **(a)** $\begin{pmatrix} -2 \\ -3 \end{pmatrix}$ **(b)** $\begin{pmatrix} -3 \\ 2 \end{pmatrix}$

(c) $\begin{pmatrix} 3 \\ -2 \end{pmatrix}$ **(d)** $\begin{pmatrix} -2 \\ -3 \end{pmatrix}$

10. **(a)** **(i)** Enlargement with centre (0, 0) and scale factor $2\frac{1}{2}$

(ii) One-way stretch parallel to the x-axis, leaving the y-axis invariant and with scale factor 2

(iii) Shear parallel to the x-axis, with the x-axis invariant and scale factor 4

(b), (c)

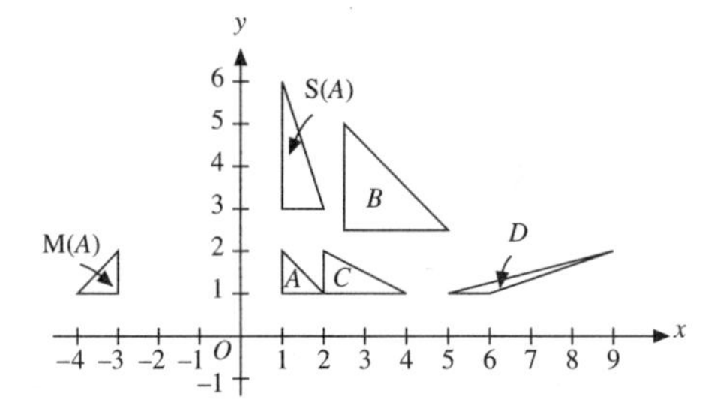

11. **(a), (b)** **(i)**

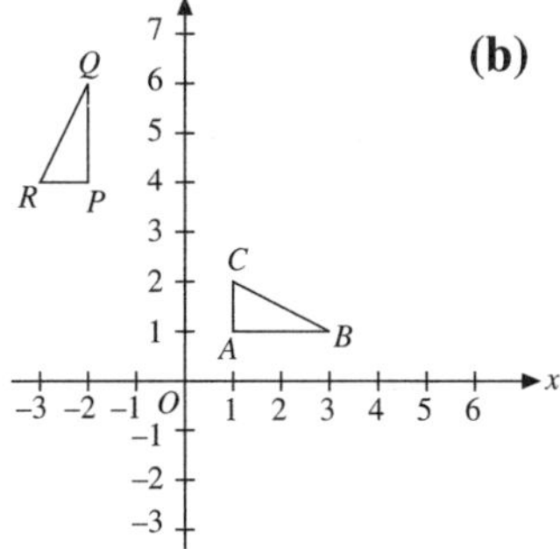

(b) **(ii)** A rotation of 90° anticlockwise about (–2, 1)

12. **(a)** **(i)** –3 **(ii)** $B_1(-3, -6)$ **(b)** $A_2(-7, 1)$ **(c)** 9

13. **(a)** **(b)** Reflection in the y-axis

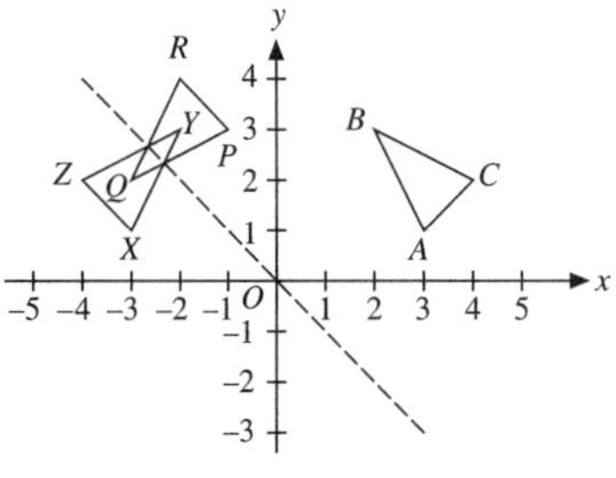

14. **(a)** (0, 2) **(b)** (–4, 8) **(c)** (6, 16) **(d)** (–1, 11)

15. **(a)** (3, 1) **(b)** **(i)** (6, 0) **(ii)** 3 **(iii)** (15, 3)

(c) **(i)** (3, 5.6) **(ii)** $\frac{1}{9}$

16. **(a)** (7, 2) **(b)** $y = \frac{1}{2}x + 3$ **(c)** **(i)** $2\frac{1}{2}$ **(ii)** $\left(12\frac{1}{2}, 2\frac{1}{2}\right)$

17. **(a)** Shear parallel to the y-axis, with factor 7

(b) Enlargement about the centre (2, 1) and factor $\frac{1}{2}$

(c) Stretch parallel to the y-axis with factor 2 and reflection in the line $y = -1$

(d) Translation $\begin{pmatrix} -5 \\ 1 \end{pmatrix}$

(e) Rotation through 180° about (4, 4)

18. **(a)** An enlargement, centre (0, 0) and scale factor 5

(b) A reflection in the line $y = x$

Chapter 4

1. $\frac{2}{5}$ **2.** $\frac{3}{5}$ **3.** **(a)** $\frac{1}{2}$ **(b)** $\frac{5}{8}$ **(c)** $\frac{1}{8}$

4. **(a)** $\frac{1}{2}$ **(b)** $\frac{1}{2}$ **(c)** $\frac{3}{8}$ **5.** **(a)** $\frac{4}{5}$ **(b)** $\frac{3}{10}$ **(c)** $\frac{2}{5}$

6. **(a)** $\frac{1}{6}$ **(b)** 1 **(c)** $\frac{1}{3}$

7. **(a)** $\frac{1}{13}$ **(b)** $\frac{1}{4}$ **(c)** $\frac{2}{13}$ **(d)** $\frac{3}{13}$ **(e)** $\frac{1}{13}$

8. **(a)** $\frac{1}{10}$ **(b)** $\frac{1}{5}$ **(c)** $\frac{3}{10}$ **9.** **(a)** $\frac{5}{36}$ **(b)** $\frac{1}{6}$

10. **(a)** $\frac{1}{221}$ **(b)** $\frac{4}{663}$ **(c)** $\frac{33}{221}$ **11.** **(a)** $\frac{3}{7}$ **(b)** $\frac{6}{7}$ **12.** $\frac{1}{156}$

13. **(a)** $\frac{5}{7}$ **(b)** **(i)** $\frac{95}{189}$ **(ii)** $\frac{94}{189}$

14. **(a)** $\frac{1}{10}$ **(b)** $\frac{1}{10}$ **(c)** $\frac{5}{12}$ **(d)** $\frac{9}{10}$

15. **(a)** $\frac{21}{40}$ **(b)** $\frac{9}{40}$

16. **(a)** **(i)** $\frac{1}{3}$ **(ii)** $\frac{1}{2}$ **(b)** **(i)** $\frac{1}{36}$ **(ii)** $\frac{1}{18}$ **(iii)** $\frac{1}{6}$

17. **(a)** $\frac{1}{6}$ **(b)** 10 **18.** **(a)** $\frac{1}{4}$ **(b)** 12 **19.** 400

20. **(a)** $\frac{1}{3}$ **(b)** $\left(\frac{2}{3}\right)^{10}$ **21.** $\frac{48}{125}$

22. **(a)** $p = \frac{1}{15}$, $q = \frac{5}{14}$, $r = 0$, $s = \frac{9}{14}$

(b) **(i)** $\frac{2}{21}$ **(ii)** 0 **(iii)** $\frac{1}{21}$

23. **(a)** $\frac{5}{26}$ **(b)** $\frac{1}{676}$

24. **(a)** $\frac{1}{6}$ **(b)** **(i)** $\frac{2}{5}$ **(ii)** $\frac{2}{15}$ **(iii)** $\frac{1}{5}$

25. **(a)** $\frac{5}{8}$ **(b)** **(i)** $\frac{1}{8}$ **(ii)** $\frac{1}{2}$

(c) **(i)** $\frac{x}{x + 16}$ **(ii)** $x = 12$

26. **(a)**

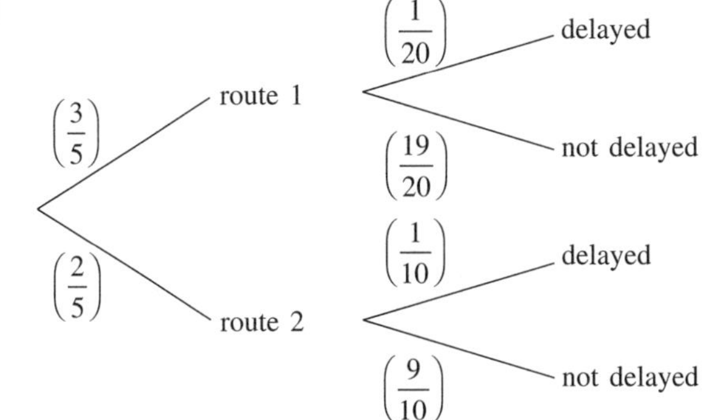

(b) **(i)** $\frac{3}{100}$ **(ii)** $\frac{93}{100}$ **(c)** $\frac{651}{5\,000}$

27. **(a)** **First disc** **Second disc**

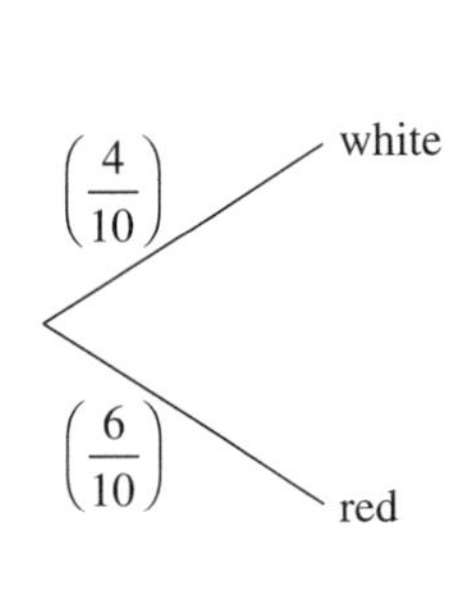

(b) **(i)** $\frac{4}{25}$ **(ii)** $\frac{1}{3}$ **(iii)** $\frac{32}{75}$ **(iv)** $\frac{38}{75}$

28. **(a)** **(i)** $\frac{5}{36}$ **(ii)** $\frac{5}{6}$

(b)

×	**1**	**2**	**3**	**4**	**5**	**6**
1	1	2	3	4	5	6
2	2	4	6	8	10	12
3	3	6	9	12	15	18
4	4	8	12	16	20	24
5	5	10	15	20	25	30
6	6	12	18	24	30	36

(c) **(i)** $\frac{1}{4}$ **(ii)** $\frac{2}{9}$

29. **(a)**

+	1	2	3	4
1	2	3	4	5
2	3	4	5	6
3	4	5	6	7
4	5	6	7	8

(b) **(i)** $\frac{1}{2}$ **(ii)** $\frac{1}{16}$ **(iii)** $\frac{5}{8}$ **(iv)** $\frac{1}{4}$

30. **(a)** $\frac{1}{8}$ **(b)** $\frac{1}{64}$ **(c)** $\frac{1}{16}$ **(d)** $\frac{3}{32}$

31. **(a)** $\frac{1}{36}$ **(b)** $\frac{2}{9}$ **(c)** $\frac{5}{18}$ **(d)** $\frac{1}{9}$

32. **(a)** **(i)** $\frac{1}{8}$ **(ii)** $\frac{1}{4}$ **(b)** $\frac{25}{64}$ **(c)** 48 cm

33. **(a)** πr^2, $9\pi r^2$ **(b)** **(i)** $\frac{1}{9}$ **(ii)** $\frac{2}{9}$

34. **(a)** $\frac{5}{9}$ **(b)** **(i)** $\frac{64}{729}$ **(ii)** $\frac{80}{243}$

35. **(a)** **(i)** 54° **(ii)** $\frac{7}{12}$ **(iii)** $\frac{4}{15}$

(b) **(i)** $\frac{3}{20}$ **(ii)** $\frac{443}{1\,800}$

36. **(a)** $\frac{1}{2}$ **(b)** $\frac{1}{2}$

37. **(a)** $\frac{3}{8}$ **(b)** $\frac{1}{8}$

38. **(a)** $\frac{1}{3}$ **(b)** **(i)** $\frac{1}{9}$ **(ii)** $\frac{5}{18}$

39. **(a)** $\frac{5}{14}$ **(b)** $\frac{15}{28}$

40. **(a)** $\frac{3}{4}$ **(b)** $\frac{1}{5}$ **(c)** $\frac{1}{5}$

41. **(a)** $\frac{1}{5}$ **(b)** **(i)** $\frac{6}{7}$ **(ii)** $\frac{22}{35}$ **(iii)** $\frac{1}{35}$ **(iv)** $\frac{12}{35}$

42. **(a)** $x = 30$ **(b)** **(i)** $\frac{9}{20}$ **(ii)** $\frac{9}{20}$

43. **(a)** $\frac{3}{8}$ **(b)** **(i)** $\frac{15}{28}$ **(ii)** $\frac{13}{28}$ **(c)** **(i)** $\frac{25}{64}$ **(ii)** $\frac{17}{32}$

44. **(a)**

Second sweet

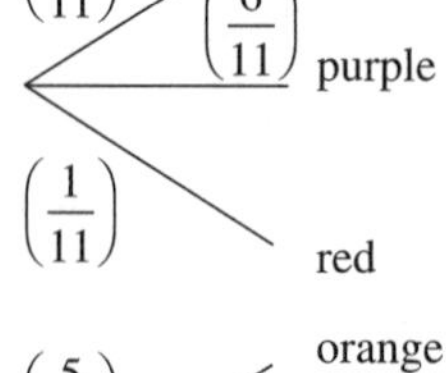

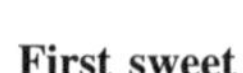

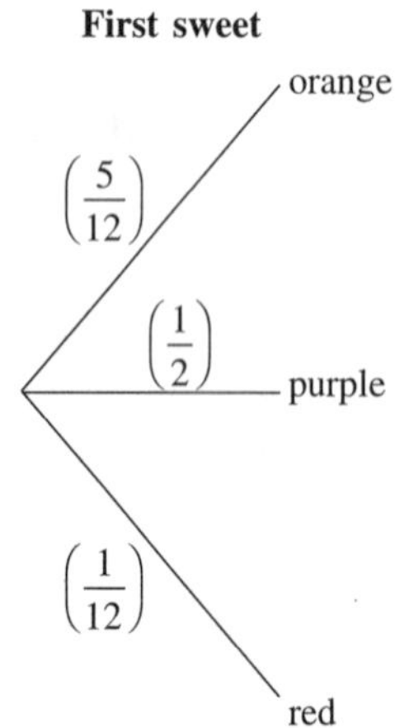

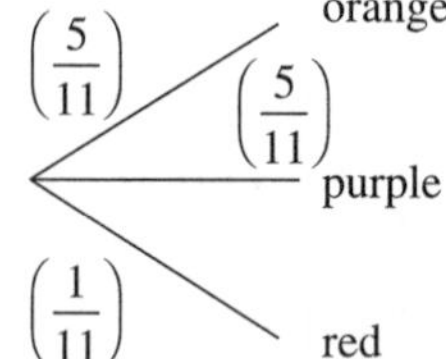

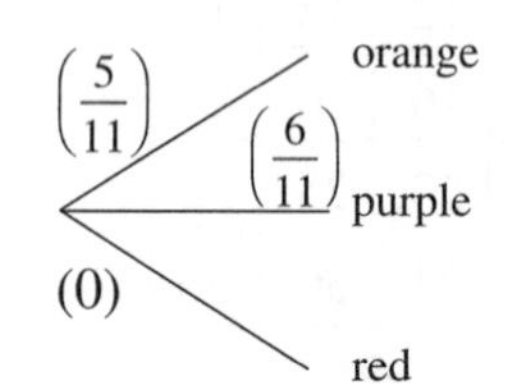

(b) **(i)** $\frac{5}{33}$ **(ii)** $\frac{41}{66}$ **(iii)** $\frac{1}{22}$ **(iv)** $\frac{5}{12}$ **(c)** $\frac{1}{12}$

45. **(a)** $\frac{3}{8}$ **(b)** $\frac{13}{28}$ **(c)** **(i)** $\frac{15}{64}$ **(ii)** $\frac{17}{64}$ **(iii)** $\frac{3}{64}$ **(iv)** 0

Test Paper 2

1. $B'(x + 2, y + 2)$

2. **(a)** **(i)** $\left(\frac{1}{2}x, \frac{1}{2}y\right)$ **(ii)** $\left(\frac{3}{4}x, \frac{3}{4}y\right)$

(b) **(i)** $(x, y + 3x)$ **(ii)** $\left(x, y - \frac{1}{3}x\right)$

(c) **(i)** $\left(x, 1\frac{2}{3}y\right)$ **(ii)** $(x, 4y)$

3. **(a)** 90° anticlockwise rotation about (0, 2)

(b) **(i)** $x = 0$ **(ii)** $\left(5\frac{1}{2}, 4\right)$

4.

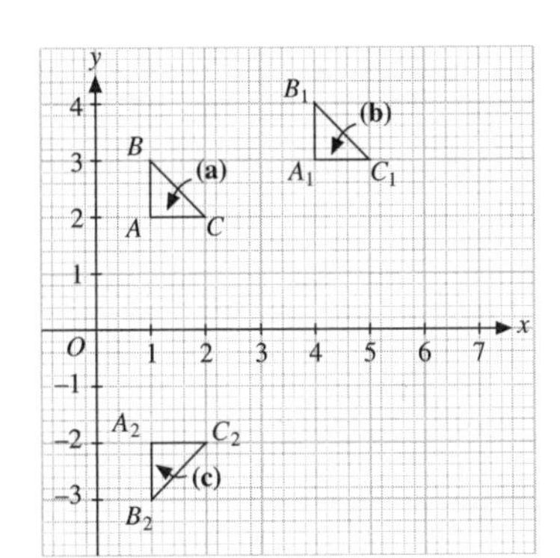

(b) Translation $\begin{pmatrix} 3 \\ 1 \end{pmatrix}$

5. **(a)** $\frac{1}{30}$ **(b)** $\frac{4}{5}$ **(c)** $\frac{1}{3}$ **6.** **(a)** $\frac{1}{36}$ **(b)** $\frac{1}{18}$ **(c)** $\frac{7}{36}$

7. **(a)** **(i)** $\frac{35}{72}$ **(ii)** $\frac{25}{144}$ **(b)** $\frac{11}{36}$ **8.** **(a)** $\frac{3}{16}$ **(b)** $\frac{7}{16}$

9. **(a)** 0.4; 0.3; 0.2 **(b)** **(i)** 0.42 **(ii)** 0.50

10. **(a)** $\frac{3}{4}$ **(b)** $\frac{3}{8}$ **(c)** $\frac{125}{216}$

Chapter 5 Revision

5.1

1. **(a)** 2 **(b)** $4\frac{1}{10}$ **2.** **(a)** 0.12 **(b)** 0.04 **(c)** –2.3

3. 12 31 **4.** **(a)** 4 **(b)** 20 **(c)** 64 **5.** $391

6. smallest: **(a)** –13 **(b)** –13

largest: **(a)** 52 **(b)** 13

7. $200

8. **(a)** 129 **(b)** 58.5% **(c)** 175

9. **(a)** \$3 700 **(b)** **(i)** $\frac{73}{100}$ **(ii)** \$2 705 **(iii)** 73.1%

(c) 78

10. **(a)** $a = 5$, $b = 25$ **(b)** $c = k + 1$, $d = (k + 1)^2$

(c) $S = n^2$ **(d)** No, 225 is not a perfect square.

5.2

1. **(a)** $\frac{1}{25}$ **(b)** 6 **(c)** 8

2. **(a)** 98 **(b)** –7 **(c)** –8

3. **(a)** 4 **(b)** $\frac{1}{4}$

4. **(a)** $y = b - 8 - 4a$ **(b)** $a = \frac{b - 8 - y}{4}$ **(c)** $b = y + 4a + 8$

5. **(a)** $\frac{77}{2}$ **(b)** $\frac{15}{4}$ **(c)** $\sqrt{50}$

6. **(a)** $(a - 1)(b - 1)$ **(b)** $(3x - 2)(2x + 3)$ **(c)** $(3x - 2)(3x + 2)$

7. **(a)** $\frac{1}{(3x + 1)(2x - 1)}$ **(b)** $y = \frac{Q + mB}{2B - 3Q}$ **(c)** $x = 1.31, 0.19$

8. 0.50, –3.00

9. **(a)** $\frac{11x - 27}{5(x - 3)(x + 3)}$

(b) **(i)** $(2x - 5)(x - 4) = 70$ **(ii)** $x = 9.21, -2.71$ **(iii)** 5.21¢

10. **(a)** $\frac{2\,400}{x}$ **(b)** $\frac{2\,400}{(x + 1)}$ **(c)** $\frac{2\,400}{x} - \frac{2\,400}{(x + 1)} = 60$

(d) $x = -6.84, 5.84$; 410.96 km/h

5.3

1. **(a)** 65° **(b)** 85° **2.** $x = 120°$, $y = 240°$

3. **(a)** 140° **(b)** 110° **4.** **(a)** 105° **(b)** 45°

5. **(a)** 28° **(b)** 56° **(c)** 28°

6. **(a)** 128.6° **(b)** 17 **7.** **(a)** 30 **(b)** 36°

8. **(a)** $\frac{9}{16}$ **(b)** $\frac{7}{9}x$

9. **(a)** 9 cm^2 **(b)** $\frac{1}{2}$ **(c)** 18 cm^2

10. **(a)** 4 **(b)** **(i)** **(ii)** 24 cm^2

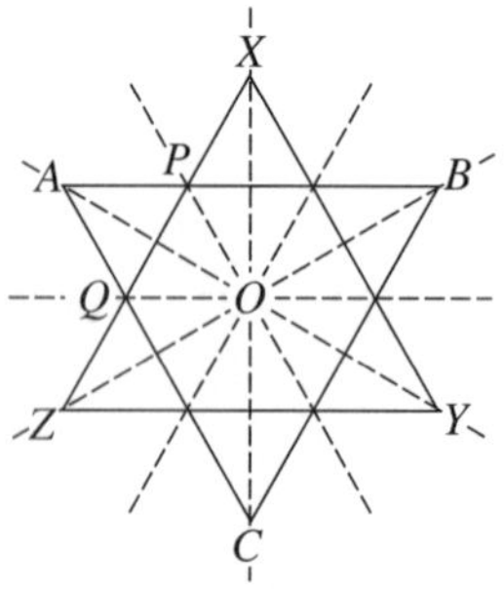

5.4

1. $m = 50\ 000$; 5×10^{10} cm^2
2. **(a)** 5π **(b)** 2.5 cm
3. **(a)** 160 cm^3 **(b)** 240 cm^3
4. **(a)** 88 cm **(b)** 55 cm **(c)** 231 cm^2
5. **(a)** $89\frac{5}{6}$ cm^2 **(b)** $46\frac{1}{3}$ cm
6. **(a)** 616 cm^2 **(b)** $718\frac{2}{3}$ cm^3
7. **(a)** 2.618 cm **(b)** 6.546 cm^2 **(c)** 7.138 cm^2
8. **(a)** $3\ 490\frac{2}{3}$ cm^3 **(b)** 1 396.27 g **(c)** 1 218.8 cm^2
9. **(a)** 144π m^2 **(c)** $r = \frac{1}{2}h$ **(d)** **(i)** 8.32 m **(ii)** 383.95π m^3
10. **(a)** 2 304 cm^3 **(b)** 4.5 cm
    (c) 1.224 kg **(d)** length = 12 cm, width = 8 cm

5.5

1. **(a)** 13 cm **(b)** $\frac{12}{13}$ **(c)** $-\frac{12}{13}$
2. **(a)** **(i)** 68.75 m **(ii)** 23.05° **(iii)** 577.5 m^2 **(b)** 50°
3. **(a)** 232° **(b)** 62° **(c)** 170°
4. **(a)** 6.71 cm **(b)** 7.78 cm **(c)** 3.96 cm **(d)** 41.6°
5. **(a)** 78.28 m **(b)** 130.72°
6. **(a)** 13 cm **(b)** 45° **(c)** $\frac{12}{5}$
7. **(a)** 32.97 m **(b)** 63.44 m **(c)** 19.9° **(d)** 57.77°
8. **(a)** 150° **(b)** 21.26 m **(c)** **(i)** 7° **(ii)** 721 m
9. **(a)** 305° **(b)** 42 km **(c)** 448.3 km^2 **(d)** 24.9 km
   (e) 7 mins
10. **(a)** $BC = 2h$ mm; $AC = 2\frac{1}{2}h$ mm **(b)** $\frac{2}{5}$ **(c)** 18 mm

5.6

1. **(a)** $AB = 11.5$ cm

2. **(a)**

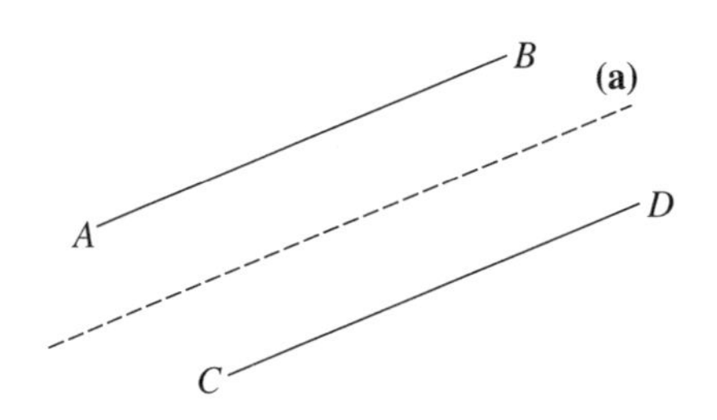

(b) The locus is a circle with AB as the diameter.

3.

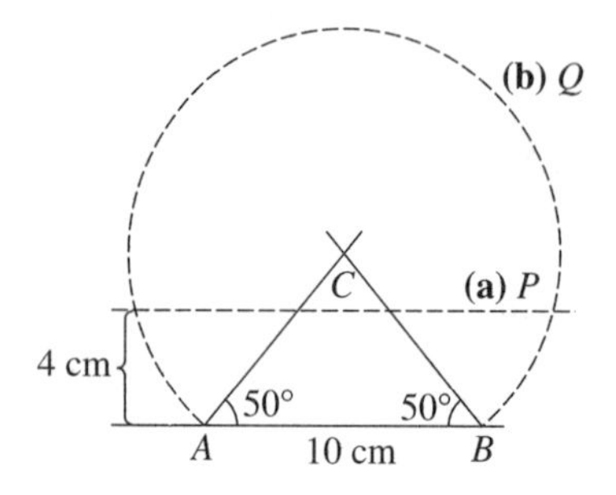

4.

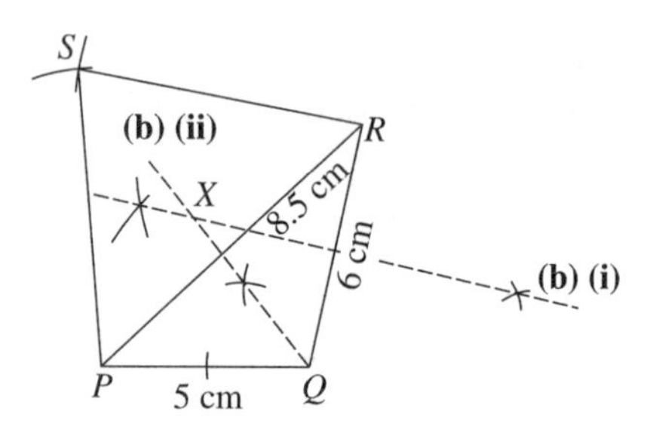

(a) $Q\hat{R}S = 88°$

(c) $SX = 4.4$ cm

5.

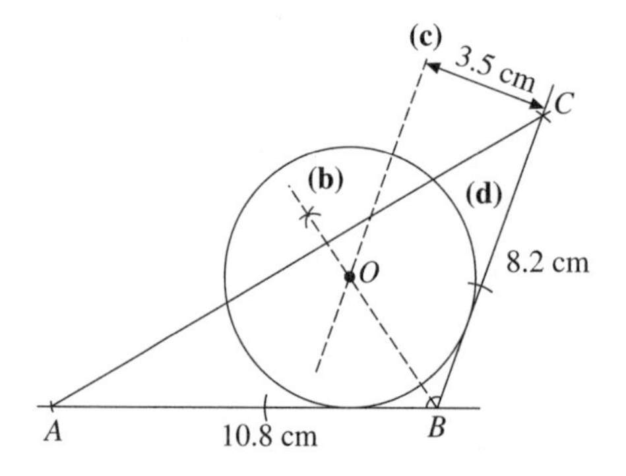

6.

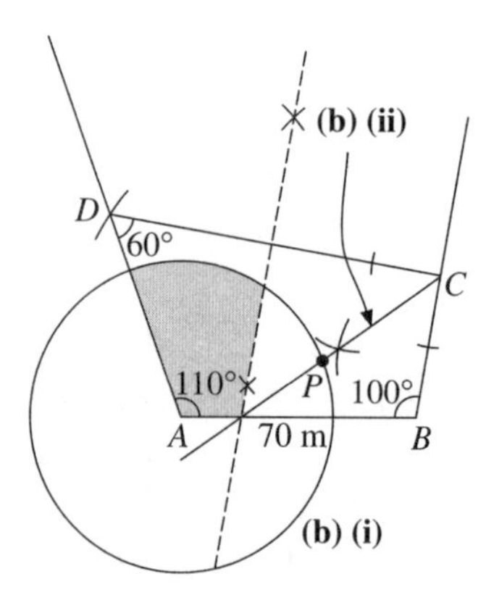

7.

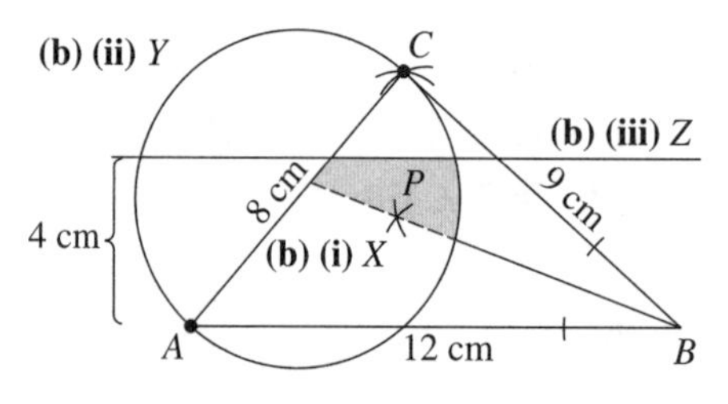

8.

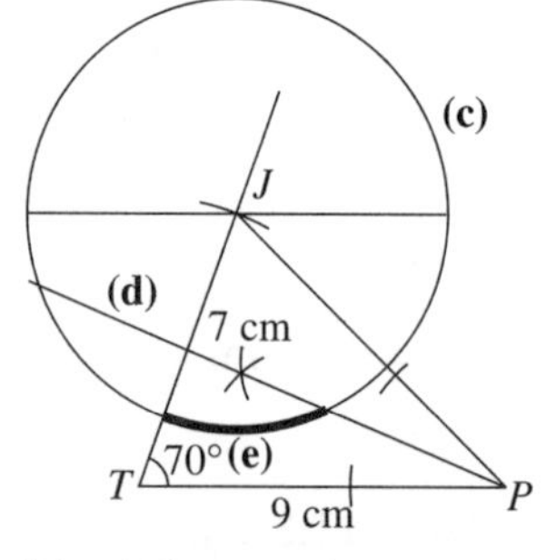

(b) Distance between Peter and John = 9.3 m

9.

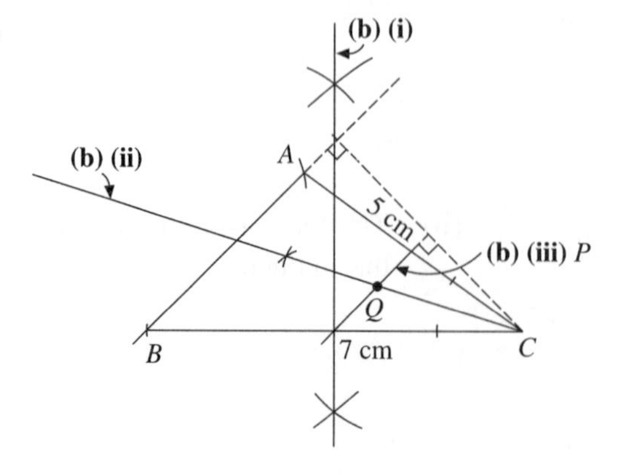

10.

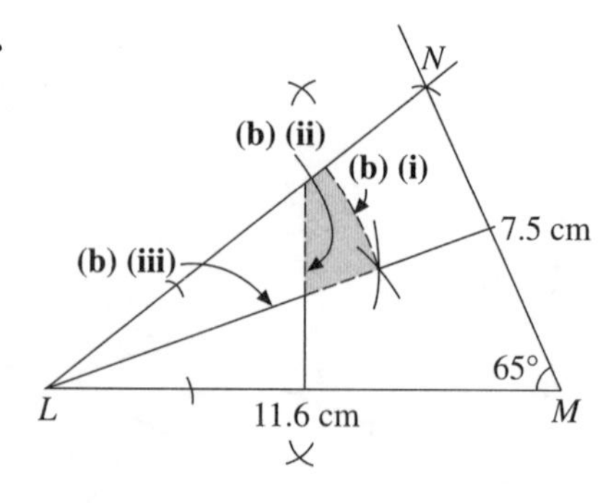

(a) $L\hat{N}M = 77°$

5.7

1. **(a)** $\begin{pmatrix} 15 \\ 21 \end{pmatrix}$ **(b)** $\begin{pmatrix} 5 \\ -4 \end{pmatrix}$ **(c)** $\begin{pmatrix} 2 \\ -2 \end{pmatrix}$

2. **(a)** **(i)** (3, –1) **(ii)** $\sqrt{10}$

   (b) $\overrightarrow{OQ} = \frac{1}{3}\mathbf{b} + \frac{2}{3}\mathbf{a}$; $\overrightarrow{BP} = \frac{1}{2}\mathbf{a} - \mathbf{b}$ **(i)** $m = \frac{4}{5}$, $n = \frac{3}{5}$ **(ii)** $\frac{1}{4}$

3. **(a)** $\begin{pmatrix} 3 \\ 4 \end{pmatrix}$ **(b)** $\sqrt{5}$ **(c)** (–1, 6)

4. **(a)** $\sqrt{20}$ **(b)** $\begin{pmatrix} 10 \\ 4 \end{pmatrix}$ **(c)** $a = \frac{5}{2}$, $b = -1$

5. **(a)** $\overrightarrow{AQ} = \frac{3}{4}\mathbf{b} - \mathbf{a}$

   (c) $(1 - k - \frac{3}{4}h)\mathbf{a} = (\frac{1}{4}h - \frac{3}{7}k)\mathbf{b}$

   $h = \frac{3}{4}$, $k = \frac{2}{3}$

   (d) $AR : RQ = 7 : 9$; $OR : OP = 3 : 4$

6. **(a)** $\overrightarrow{CA} = -2\mathbf{b} - 2\mathbf{a}$ **(b)** $\overrightarrow{AF} = h(\mathbf{b} + 2\mathbf{a})$; $\overrightarrow{CF} = k(-2\mathbf{b} - \mathbf{a})$

   (c) $(2 - 2h - k)\mathbf{a} = (h + 2k - 2)\mathbf{b}$

   $h = \frac{2}{3}$, $k = \frac{2}{3}$

   (d) 6

   (e) $\overrightarrow{BF} = \frac{2}{3}(\mathbf{b} - \mathbf{a})$, $\overrightarrow{BM} = (\mathbf{b} - \mathbf{a})$, $\frac{\overrightarrow{BF}}{\overrightarrow{BM}} = \frac{2}{3}$ $\therefore$ B, F and M are collinear.

7. **(a)** **(i)** $2\mathbf{a}$ **(ii)** $\mathbf{b} + \mathbf{a}$ **(iii)** $2\mathbf{b} - \mathbf{a}$

   (b) $h(2\mathbf{b} - \mathbf{a})$ **(c)** $k(-2\mathbf{a} - \mathbf{b})$

   (d) $(2h + k - 1)\mathbf{b} = (1 - 2k + h)\mathbf{a}$

   $h = \frac{1}{5}$, $k = \frac{3}{5}$

   (e) $\frac{1}{4}$

8. **(a)** **(i)** $\mathbf{a}$ **(ii)** $\mathbf{b} - 3\mathbf{a}$ **(iii)** $2\mathbf{a} + \mathbf{b}$

   (b) $\overrightarrow{PQ} = \overrightarrow{PA} + \overrightarrow{AQ} = 2\mathbf{a} + k\overrightarrow{AC} = 2\mathbf{a} + k(\mathbf{b} - 3\mathbf{a}) = (2 - 3k)\mathbf{a} + k\mathbf{b}$

   (c) $h = \frac{2}{5}$, $k = \frac{2}{5}$

9. **(a)** **(i)** $\frac{1}{2}\mathbf{b}$ **(ii)** $\frac{1}{2}\mathbf{b} - \mathbf{c}$

   (b) $\overrightarrow{DE} = (h - \frac{1}{4})\mathbf{c} + \frac{1}{8}\mathbf{b}$ **(c)** **(i)** $\frac{1}{4}$ **(ii)** $\frac{1}{8}$ **(iii)** $\frac{1}{32}$

10. **(a)** **(i)** $\mathbf{b} - 2\mathbf{a}$ **(ii)** $\frac{1}{3}\mathbf{b} - \frac{2}{3}\mathbf{a}$ **(iii)** $\frac{2}{3}\mathbf{b} - \frac{1}{3}\mathbf{a}$

    (b) $\frac{ST}{TR} = \frac{1}{2}$, $\therefore$ S, T, R form a straight line, $\therefore$ ST produced will pass through R.

    (c) $\sqrt{29}$

5.8

1. **(a)** 7

   (b) **(i)** $y = \frac{6}{5}x - 6$ **(ii)** 25 units^2 **(iii)** $(-5, -2)$

2. **(a)** $-\frac{3}{4}$ **(b)** $y = \frac{3}{4}x - 6$ **(c)** 27 units^2

3. **(a)** $a + 2b = 16$; $a = 10$; $b = 3$ **(b)** $(0, 10)$

4. **(a)** 1.43

   (b) Draw the line $y = 3$, $x = 2.7, 5.55$

   (c) $2 < x < 7.55$

5. $a = -4$, $b = 16$

   (a) **(i)** -20

   (ii) $x = -1.65, 0, 1.65$

   (b) 12

   (c) Draw $y = 5x + 4$,

   $x = -2.4, -0.8, 3.3$

   (d) 27.8 units^2

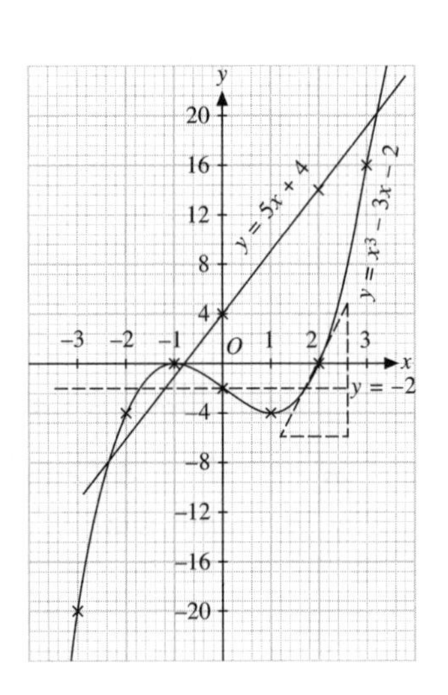

6. **(a)** $a = -1.71$, $b = 1.5$

   (c) $x = -1.2, 0.5$

   (d) Draw $y = \frac{1}{2}(x + 1)$,

   $-2.5 \leqslant x \leqslant 0.6$

   (e) 3.1 units^2

7. **(a)**

x	–1	–0.5	0	0.5	1	2	3
y	–0.5	–0.3	–0.3	0.41	1	3	7

(b)

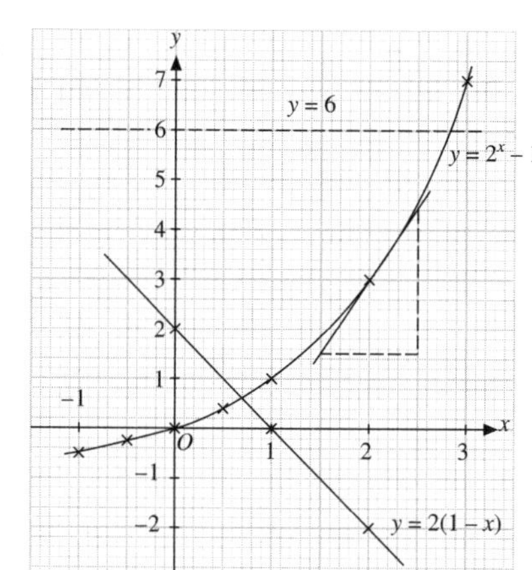

(c) $x = 2.8$

(d) (0.7, 0.6)

(e) 3

8. **(a)** 2 m/s^2 **(b)** 260 m **(c)** 30.5 s

9. **(a)** 80 km/h **(b)** 80 min **(c)** 100 km/h

10. **(a)** 25 m/s **(b)** 450 m **(c)** 66 m/s **(d)** 45 m

5.9

1. **(a)** $x = 6$ **(b)** –2 **(c)** $\begin{pmatrix} 8 \\ -9 \end{pmatrix}$

(d) Anticlockwise 90° rotation with (–2, 0) as the centre

(e) Stretch with factor 2 and the x-axis as the invariant line

2. **(a)**

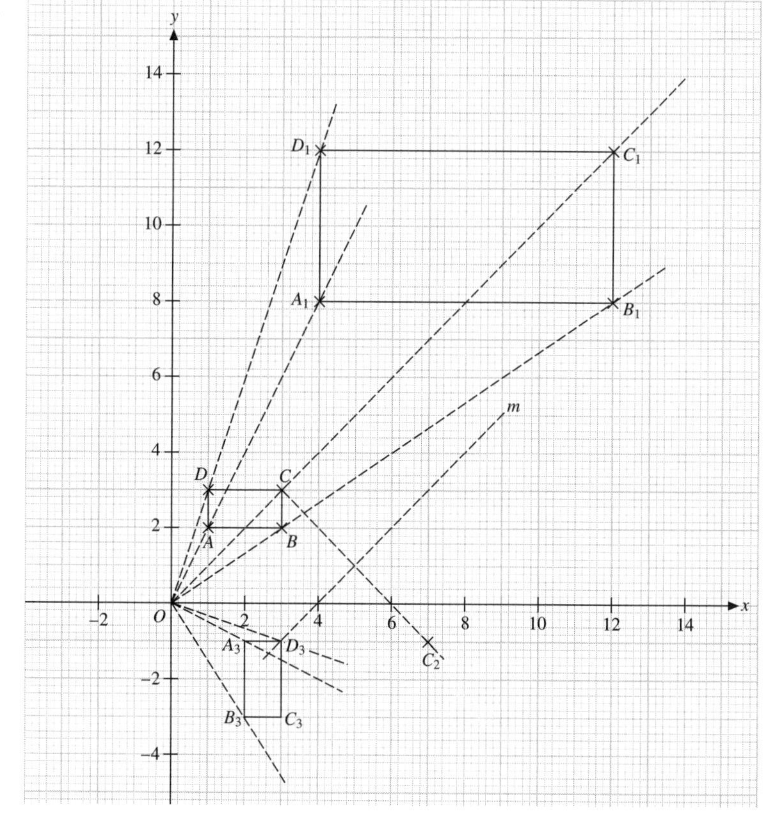

(b) **(ii)** scale factor = 4

(c) $y = x - 4$

3. 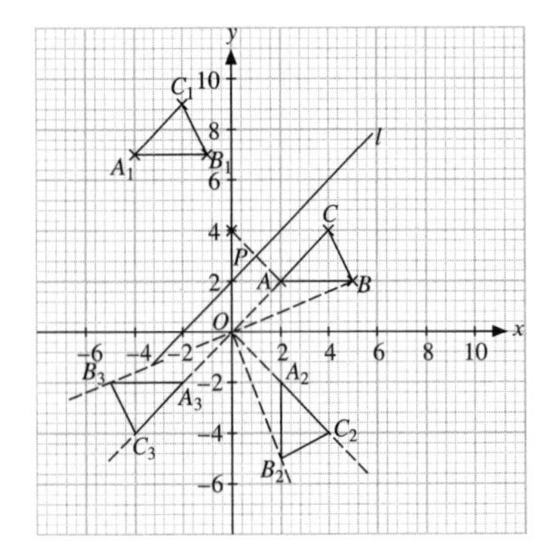

(b) $y = x + 2$

(f) $90°$ clockwise rotation about the origin

4. 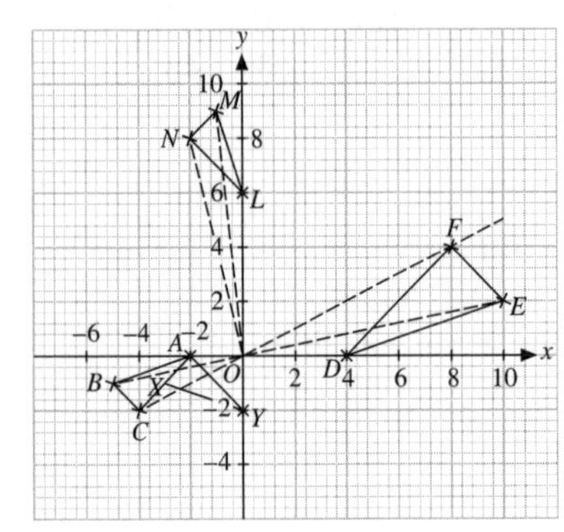

(a) **(ii)** -2

(b) **(i)** $90°$ clockwise

(ii) $\begin{pmatrix} -1 \\ 3 \end{pmatrix}$

(c) **(i)** -2

(iii) Shear with factor -2 and x-axis as the invariant line

(d) 4

5. **(a)** $\begin{pmatrix} 3 \\ 1 \end{pmatrix}$

(b) $x + y = 5$

(c) Shear with factor 2 and the x-axis as the invariant line

6. 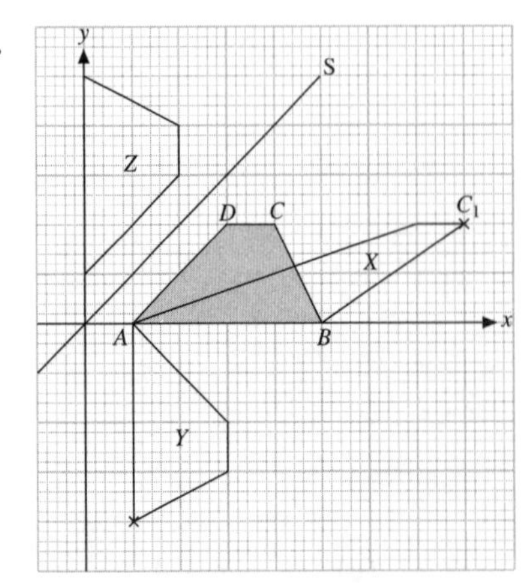

7. **(a)** $\begin{pmatrix} -2 \\ -4 \end{pmatrix}$

(b) $y = x$

(d) Shear with factor 2 and the x-axis as the invariant line

(e) Enlargement with (1, 0) as centre and factor 2

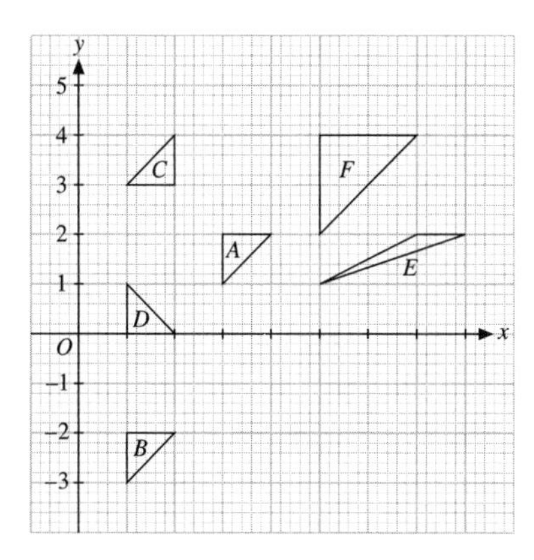

8. 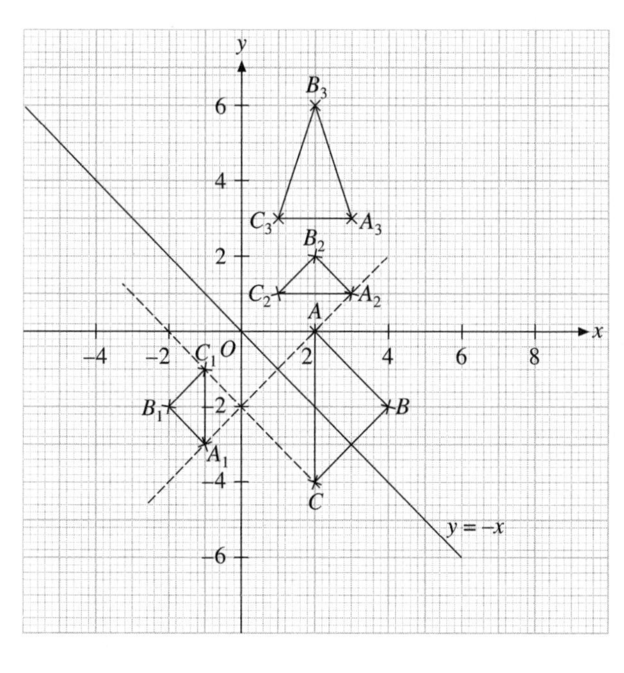

(d) (2, 6)

9. **(b)** P is an enlargement with (2, 1) as centre and scale factor –2.

(c) (0, 1)

(e) **(i)** $A_3(-4, 2)$, $B_3(-3, 2)$, $C_3\left(-\frac{1}{2}, 1\right)$, $D_3\left(-1\frac{1}{2}, 1\right)$

(ii) Q is a shear with factor $-2\frac{1}{2}$ and the x-axis as the invariant line.

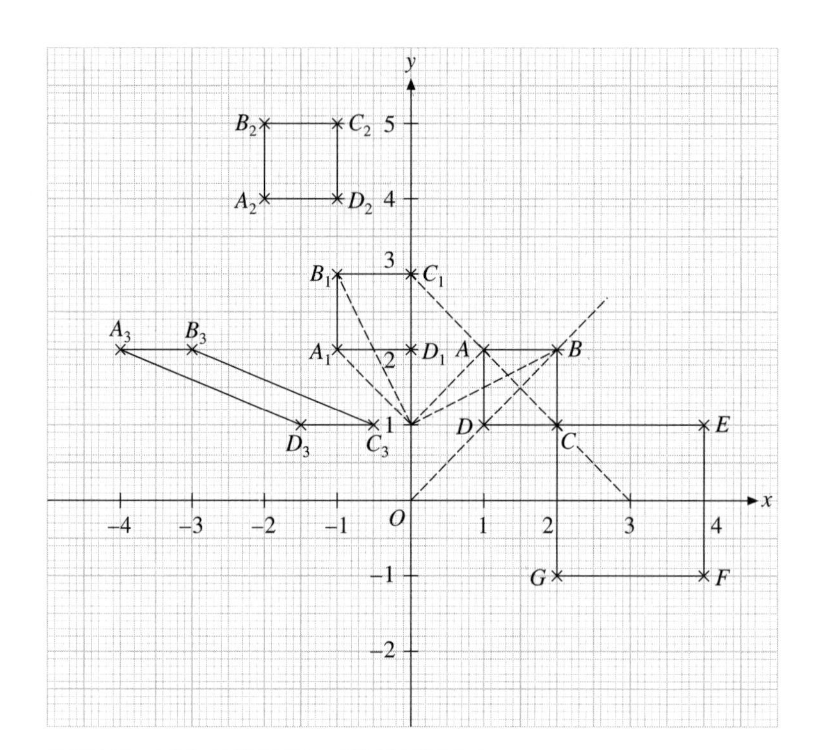
y
x
O
B_2 C_2
A_2 D_2
B_1 C_1
A_1 D_1
A_3 B_3
D_3 C_3
A B
D C E
G F
5
4
3
2
1
–1
–2
–4 –3 –2 –1 1 2 3 4

10.

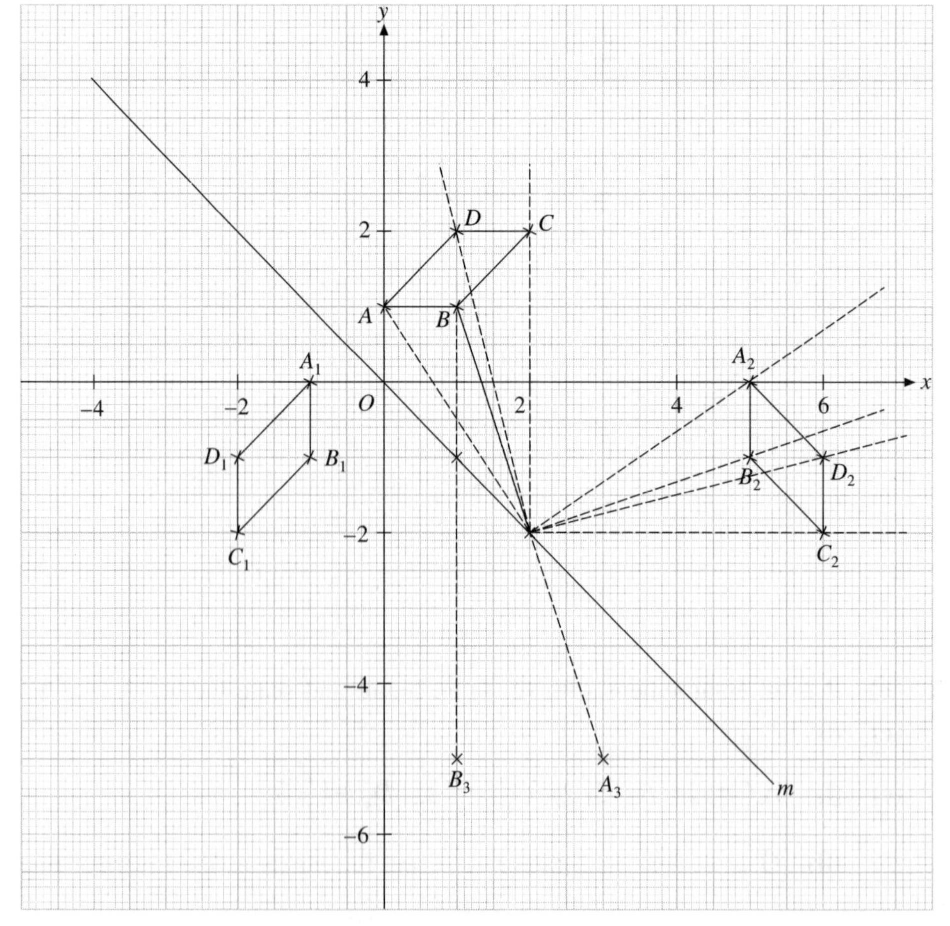
y
x
O
m
D C
A B
A_1
D_1 B_1
C_1
A_2
B_2 D_2
C_2
B_3 A_3
4
2
–2
–4
–6
–4 –2 2 4 6

(c) **(ii)** Reflection in the line $x = 2$
(d) **(i)** $(1, -1)$
(ii) -2
(e) **(i)** x-axis or $y = 0$
(ii) $(2, 1)$

5.10

1. **(a)** **(i)** 1 **(ii)** 2 **(b)** 6

2. **(a)** 72° **(b)** 1.65 **(c)** $\frac{9}{16}$

3. **(a)** 50 s **(b)** 20.5 s **(c)** 73 **(d)** 80

4.

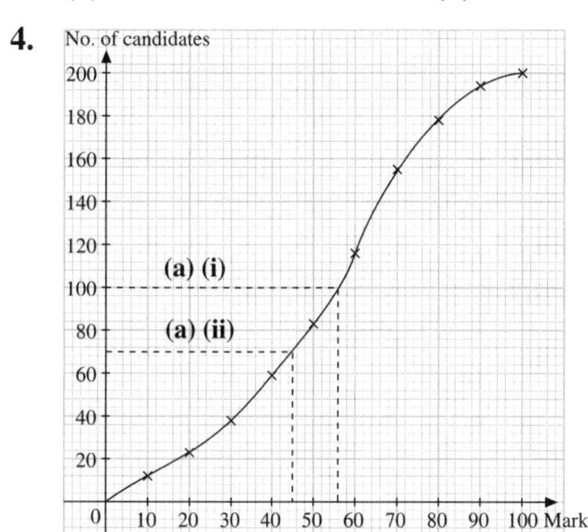

(a) **(i)** 56
(ii) 45
(b) **(i)** $\frac{1}{3}$
(ii) $\frac{5}{18}$

5.

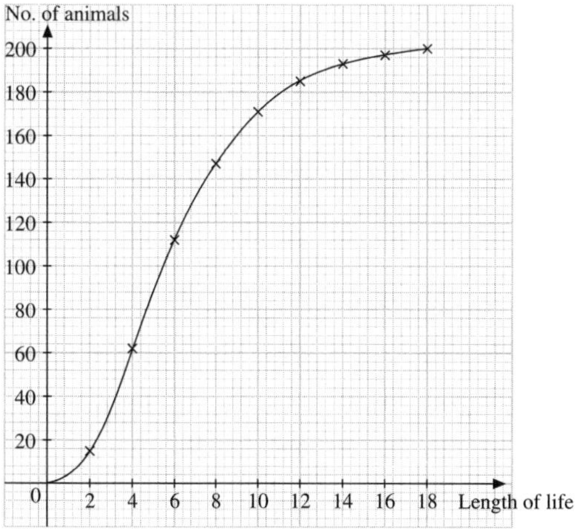

(a)

2	4	6	8	10	12	14	16	18
15	62	112	147	171	185	193	197	200

(b) **(i)** 5.6 **(ii)** 4.8

(c) **(i)** $\frac{3}{40}$ **(ii)** $\frac{13}{40}$

6. (a) **First draw** **Second draw**

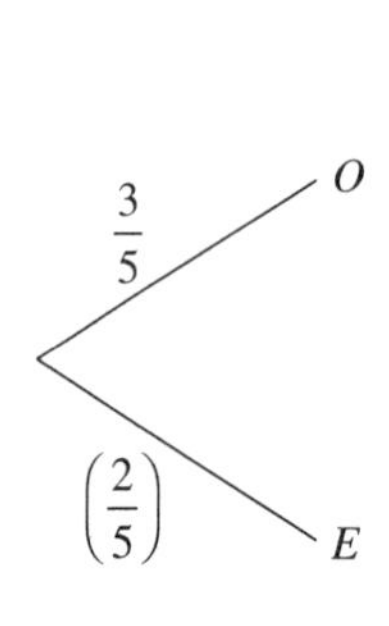

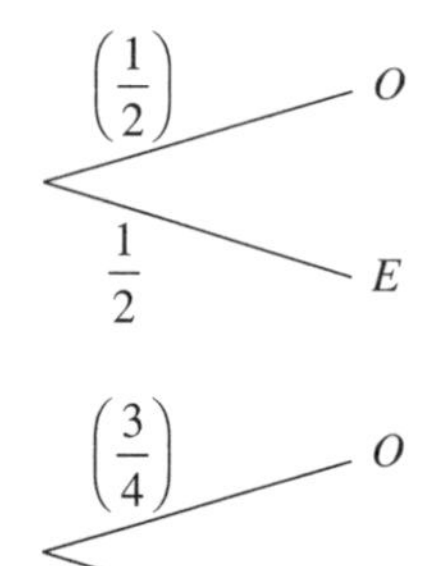

(b) $\frac{1}{10}$ **(c)** $\frac{3}{5}$ **(d)** $\frac{1}{10}$

7. (a) (i) $\frac{5}{33}$ **(ii)** $\frac{1}{22}$ **(iii)** $\frac{1}{220}$ **(b)** 1

8. (a) $\frac{3}{8}$ **(b) (i)** $\frac{7}{8}$ **(ii)** $\frac{15}{64}$

9. (a) (i) 2 **(ii)** 3 **(iii)** 6

(b) (i) $\frac{1}{16}$ **(ii)** $\frac{1}{16}$ **(iii)** $\frac{1}{16}$

(iv) $\frac{1}{16}$ **(v)** $\frac{1}{16}$ **(vi)** $\frac{1}{4}$

(c) 1

10. (a)

–	1	2	3	4	5
1	0	1	2	3	4
2	1	0	1	2	3
3	2	1	0	1	2
4	3	2	1	0	1
5	4	3	2	1	0

(b) (i) $\frac{13}{25}$ **(ii)** $\frac{2}{5}$

Assessment Paper Set A (Paper 1)

1. (a) $3\frac{11}{15}$ **(b)** 26 640 **(c)** 0.4

2. (a) $3x(9x - 4)$ **(b)** $(3 + 4y^8)(3 - 4y^8)$ **(c)** $(w - 12)(w + 2)$

3. (a) 23° **(b)** 44° **(c)** 67°

4. (a) $y = 8\sqrt{x}$ **(b) (i)** $30\frac{1}{4}$ **(ii)** 3.2

5. (a) 118 **(b)** 30 **(c)** 3 : 1

6. $x = 6$, $y = 2$

7. (a) $\frac{1}{6}$ **(b)** 50

8. (a) $\frac{16}{81}$ **(b)** 8 **(c)** 19

9. **(a)** 3 **(b)** –5 or 6

10. **(a)** 4 **(b)** 28 **(c)** $2\frac{1}{4}$

11. **(a)** $\frac{4}{9}$, $\frac{7}{16}$, 43%, 0.4 **(b)** –4, –2, –1, 0

12. **(a)** 305° **(b)** 025° **(c)** 075°

13. **(a)** 16 cm **(b)** 51.2 cm^3

14. **(a)** $24\frac{1}{2}$ cm^2 **(b)** 14 cm^2

15. **(a)** 1.61×10^{-2} **(b)** 7.5×10^{-11}

16. 84°, 126°, 210°

17. **(a)** $T = 2$ **(b)** 40 m/s^2

18. **(a)** 30 coins **(b)** 10%

19. **(a)** $\frac{4}{13}$ **(b)** 5 cm **(c)** 168 cm^3

20. **(a) (i), (b) (i)** **(a) (ii)** $y = 1.5$
(b) (ii) (4.5, 0.5)

21. **(a)**

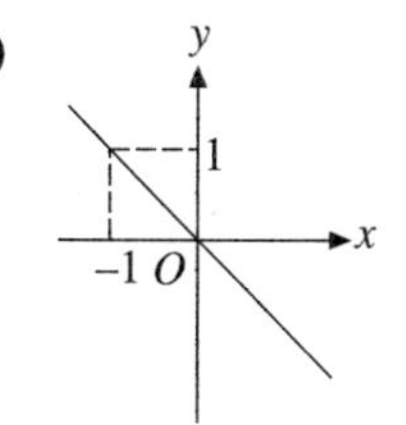

(b)

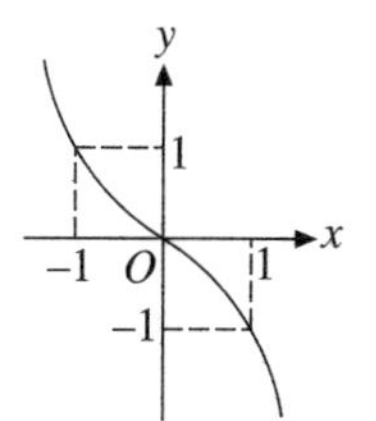

(c)

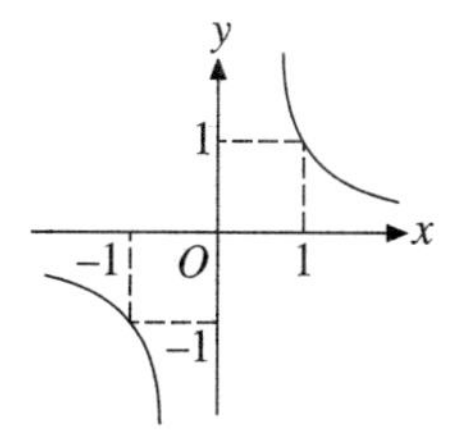

22.

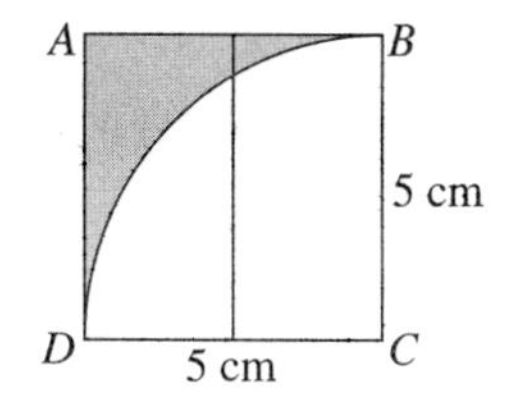

23. **(a)** 24
(b) $\frac{19}{24}$
(c) $\frac{13}{114}$

24. **(a)** $N = 4$, $T = 16$
$N = 5$, $T = 25$
(b) $T = N^2$ **(c)** **(i)** 121 **(ii)** 625

25. **(a)** $\sqrt{73}$ **(b)** $a = 6$, $b = 23$ **(c)** $c = 1$, $d = 12$

26. **(a)** 144° **(b)** 5, 8

(c)

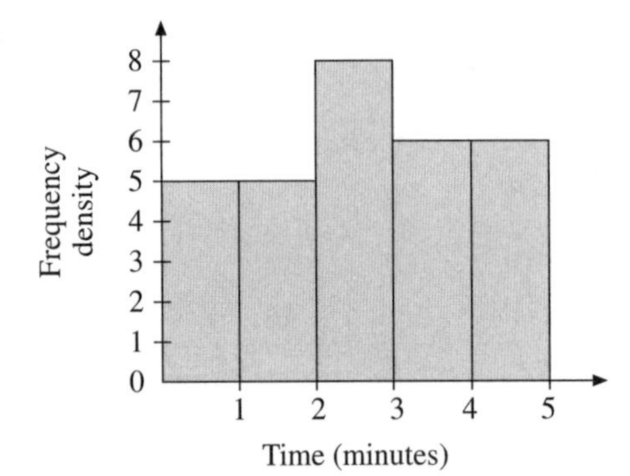

27. **(a)** (–3, 0) **(b)** (7, 0) **(c)** (0, 3)

28. **(a)** 2

(b) **(i)** 9, $\frac{1}{9}$

(ii) $y = \frac{1}{9}x + 5\frac{1}{9}$

Assessment Paper Set A (Paper 2)

1. **(a)** 5.33 cm **(b)** 5.19 cm **(c)** 20.4°

2. **(a)** 0.246 or –3.25 **(b)** $\frac{15 - 4x}{x(2x - 3)}$ **(c)** $\frac{2x}{xy - 3}$

(d) $r = \frac{3q(q - 1)}{q - 3}$

3. **(a)** **(i)** 2 443.8 km **(ii)** $1 467.03

(b) **(i)** 540° **(ii)** 49° **(iii)** 41°

(iv) 84° **(v)** 75.5

4. **(a)** **(i)** 8.06 units **(ii)** $\begin{pmatrix} 14\frac{1}{2} \\ 10 \end{pmatrix}$

(b) **(i)** $\frac{2}{3}$ **(ii)** $\frac{1}{4}$ **(iii)** $\frac{1}{9}$

(c) 36 cm^2

5. **(a)** $3 050 **(b)** $1 830 **(c)** $1 873

6. **(a)** 18.3 cm **(b)** 64.2 cm^2 **(c)** 51.9 cm^2

(d) 1 557.5 cm^3 **(e)** 4 620 cm^3 **(f)** 23.5 kg

7. **(a)** Shrub $52, Tree $88

(b) **(i)** $(140 – s) **(ii)** $\frac{1\,000}{140 - s}$; Shrub $40, Tree $100

8. **(a)** 68.4° **(b)** 111.6° **(c)** 301 m^2

(d) 23.4 m **(e)** 114.6 m **(f)** 666.5 m^2

9. **(a)**

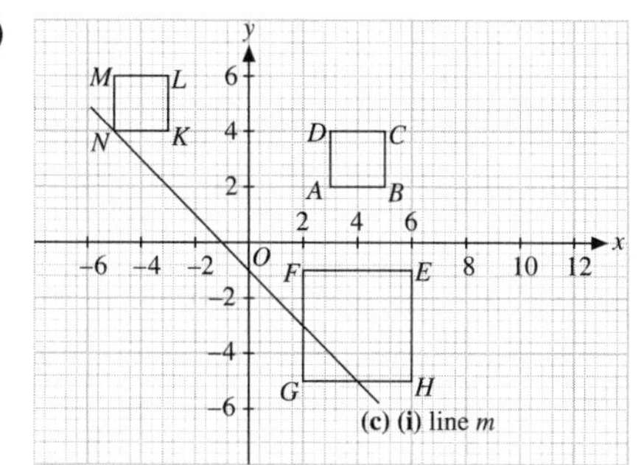

(b) **(i)** (4, 1) **(ii)** –2 **(iii)** $\frac{1}{4}$

(c) **(ii)** $x + y + 1 = 0$

(iii) Anticlockwise rotation through 90° about (–1, 0)

10. **(a)** $a = 2.6$, $b = -2.6$

(b)

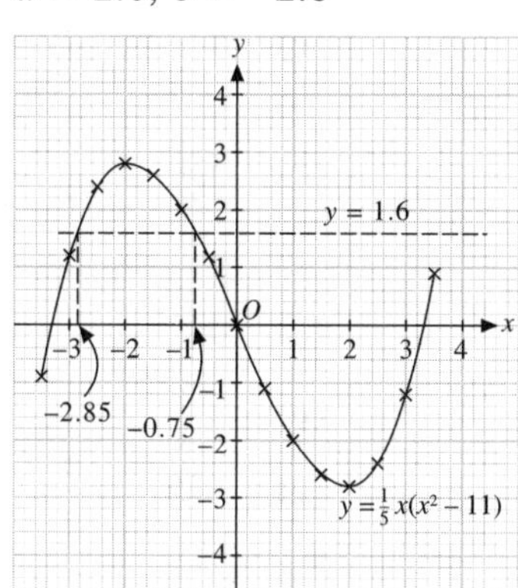

(c) $x = -2.85, -0.75$

(d) **(i)** $-1.9 < x < 1.9$

(ii) $-3.3 < x < 0$, $x > 3.3$

11. **(a)** **(i)** $3\mathbf{p}$ **(ii)** $3\mathbf{p} - \mathbf{q}$ **(iii)** $\mathbf{q} - 2\mathbf{p}$ **(iv)** $\frac{3}{4}(\mathbf{p} + \mathbf{q})$

(b) **(i)** $h(\mathbf{q} - 2\mathbf{p})$ **(c)** $h = \frac{2}{3}$, $k = \frac{8}{9}$

(d) $\frac{1}{9}$ **(e)** **(i)** $22\frac{1}{2}$ cm^2 **(ii)** 5 cm^2

12. **(a)** 57, 235, 295

(b)

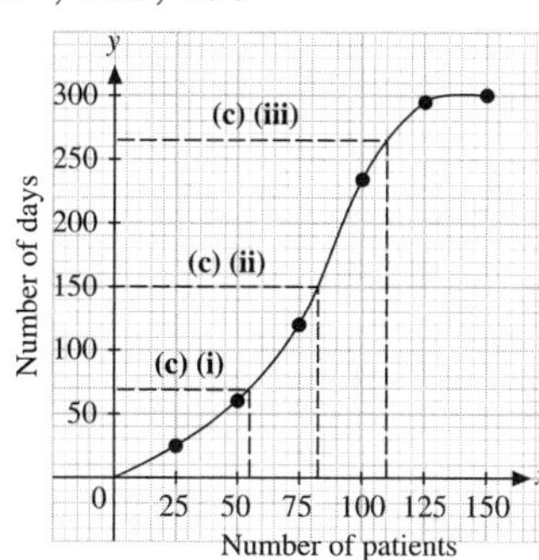

(c) **(i)** 65 **(ii)** 83 **(iii)** 11%

(d) $\frac{39}{100}$ **(e)** $\frac{1}{3\ 600}$

Assessment Paper Set B (Paper 1)

1.	**(a)** 0.029 4	**(b)** $16\frac{2}{3}$	
2.	**(a)** 7	**(b)** –54	**(c)** 33
3.	**(a)** 6.3×10^{-3}	**(b)** 32.5%	**(c)** $\frac{27}{200}$
4.	**(a)** \$8.16		
	(b) **(i)** 8 packets	**(ii)** \$26	
5.	**(a)** $2a(a^2 + 9)$	**(b)** $(3x + 1)(x - 2)$	
6.	**(a)** $\frac{17}{20}$	**(b)** $\frac{1}{2}$	
7.	**(a)** 20	**(b)** $1\frac{2}{13}$	
8.	**(a)** $\frac{1}{81}$	**(b)** 2	**(c)** 8
9.	**(a)** $x \leqslant -1$	**(b)** –3, –2, –1, 0	
10.	**(a)** 50°	**(b)** 45°	**(c)** 55°
11.	$x = \frac{1}{3}$, $y = -3$		
12.	**(a)** RT	**(b)** 121.5°	**(c)** 027°
13.	**(a)** 5 cm	**(b)** $\frac{12}{13}$	**(c)** $-\frac{5}{8}$
14.	**(a)** 10	**(b)** –12	**(c)** –35
15.	**(a)** 6 mins 40 secs	**(b)** 61 : 77	
16.	**(a)** $x = \frac{16}{49}$	**(b)** $y = -5$	
17.	**(a)** 40°	**(b)** 60°	**(c)** 20°
18.	**(a)** \$69.45	**(b)** \$9.60	**(c)** \$1 910
19.	**(a)** 2	**(b)** 2.1	
20.	**(a)** 12	**(b)** $z = \frac{1}{2}$ or $-\frac{1}{2}$	
21.	**(a)** $\begin{pmatrix} -26 \\ 1 \end{pmatrix}$	**(b)** 17	**(c)** $-3\frac{1}{5}$
22.	**(a)** 14 m/s	**(b)** $43\frac{5}{9}$ m/s	
23.	**(a)** **(i)** $8x$ m	**(ii)** $\frac{5x^2}{2}$ m^2	
	(b) **(i)** 2.5 cm	**(ii)** 6 cm	
24.	**(a)** $\frac{1}{2}$	**(b)** $y = \frac{1}{2}x + 2$	**(c)** 12
25.	**(a)** Enlargement with centre (1, 0) and scale factor –2		
	(b) Shear parallel to the y-axis with shear factor 2		
26.	**(a)** 17.32 cm^2	**(b)** 7 cm	
27.	**(a)** 4 : 5		
	(b) **(i)** 12.5 kg	**(ii)** 500 cm^3	

28.

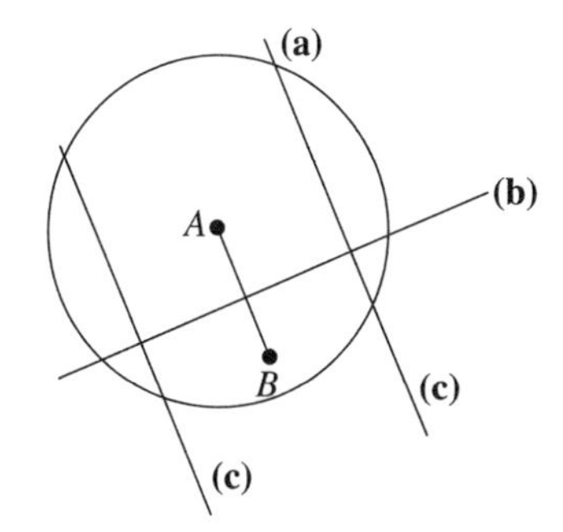

29. **(a)** $\frac{4}{5}$ **(b)** $\frac{5}{12}$ **(c)** **(i)** $\frac{4}{45}$ **(ii)** $\frac{14}{45}$

Assessment Paper Set B (Paper 2)

1. **(a)** 8% **(b)** **(i)** \$45 400 **(ii)** \$17 252 **(iii)** \$652.63
(c) \$1 875 **(d)** \$62 500

2. **(a)** $\frac{9 + 7x - 2x^2}{(2x - 1)(3 + 2x)}$

(b) **(i)** $d = 2\frac{3}{4}$ **(ii)** $e = 3.29$ or 0.71 **(c)** $y = \frac{x - 1}{x + 1}$

3. **(a)** 7.14 cm **(b)** 45.6° **(c)** 7.55 cm **(d)** 125° **(e)** 4.13 cm

4. **(a)** **(i)** 41° **(ii)** 107°

(b) **(i)** $B\hat{X}C = A\hat{X}D$ (vert. opp. ∠s)
$B\hat{C}X = A\hat{D}X$ (∠s in the same segment)
$\therefore \triangle BCX$ is similar to $\triangle ADX$.

(ii) 5.6 cm

(iii) $\frac{9}{16}$

5. **(a)**

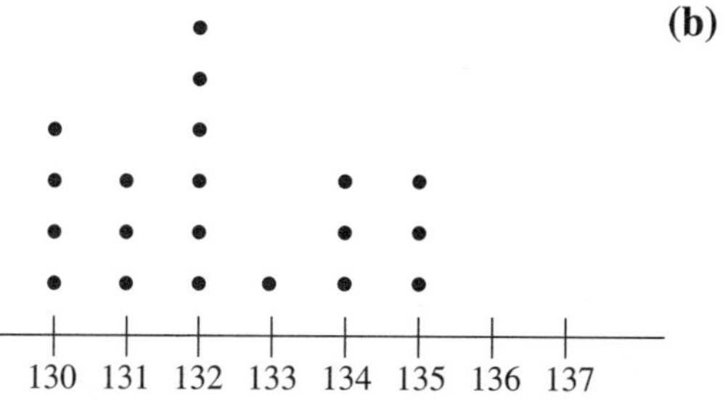

(b) 132 cm

(c)

Stems	Leaf
5	8
6	3 5 7 9
7	0 4 4 4 4 6 6 8
8	0 4 5
9	0 2 3 8

(d) 58; 98 **(e)** 74

(f) The cluster is at 74 and the gap is between 58 and 63.

6. **(a)** **(i)** 7.00 cm **(ii)** 23.6 cm

(b) **(i)** **(1)** 18π cm^3 **(2)** 10 cm **(ii)** $3\frac{1}{3}$ cm

7. **(a)** $x = 17$ **(b)** **(i)** $\frac{42}{x}$ h **(ii)** $\frac{42}{x+2}$ h

(b) **(iii)** $\frac{42}{x} - \frac{42}{x+2} = \frac{1}{3}$ **(iv)** 14.9 or –16.9; 2 h 49 mins

8. **(a)**

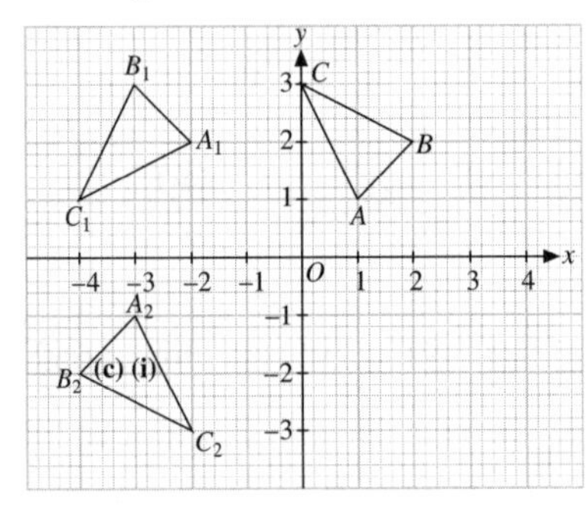

(b) **(i)** 90° **(ii)** $\begin{pmatrix} -1 \\ 1 \end{pmatrix}$ **(iii)** (–1, 0)

(c) **(i)** Rotation through 180° about (–1, 0)

9. **(a)** –2.25

(b)

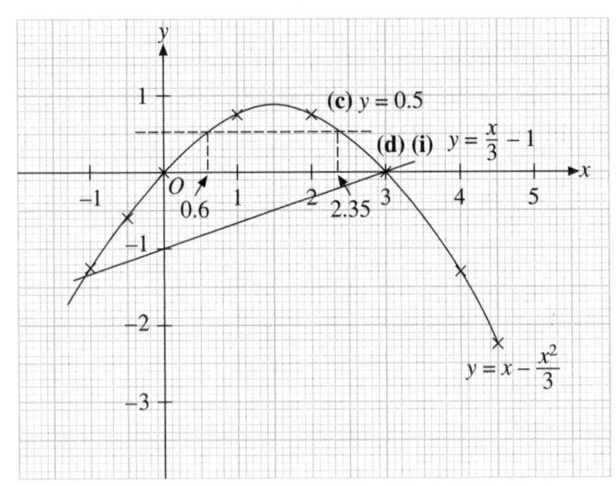

(c) 0.6 or 2.35 **(d)** **(ii)** –1 or 3 **(iii)** $(x + 1)(x - 3) = 0$

10. **(a)** **(i)** 135° **(ii)** $22\frac{1}{2}°$ **(b)** **(i)** $PR = 11.9$ cm

(b)

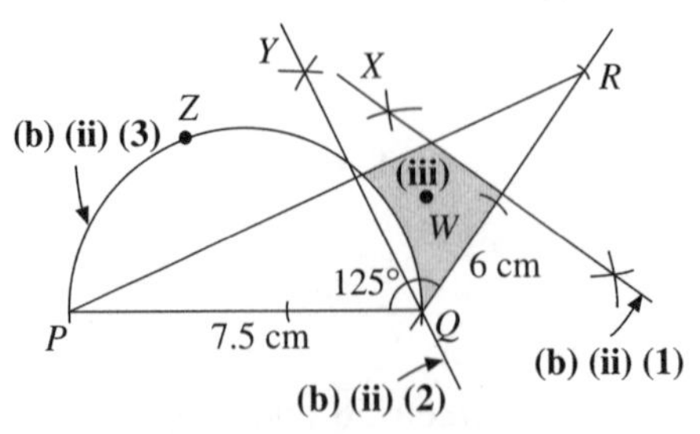

11. **(a)** 80

(b)

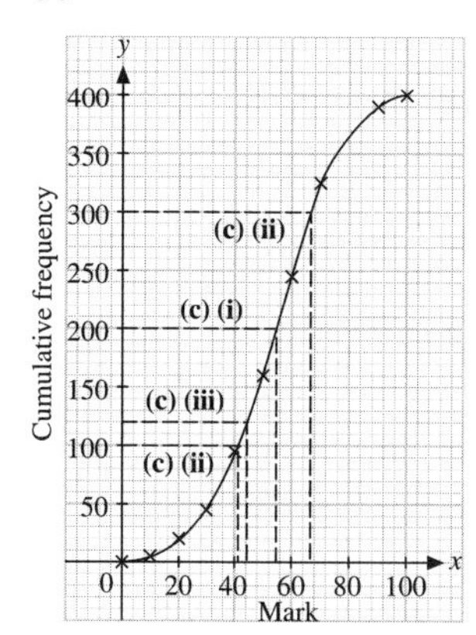

(c) **(i)** 55 **(ii)** 25 **(iii)** 70%

(d) **(i)** 80 **(ii)** $\frac{4}{5}$ **(e)** $\frac{19}{500}$

12. **(a)** **(i)** $4\mathbf{a} + 3\mathbf{b}$ **(ii)** $3\mathbf{b} - 4\mathbf{a}$ **(iii)** $2\mathbf{a} - 3\mathbf{b}$

(b) $2h\mathbf{a} - 3h\mathbf{b}$ **(d)** $4k\mathbf{a} + 3k\mathbf{b}$ **(e)** $h = \frac{4}{3}$, $k = \frac{1}{3}$

(f) 2 : 1 **(g)** $\frac{2}{3}$